Gemstones of Northern England

by

Peter R. Rodgers

Dalesman Books

1981

The Dalesman Publishing Company Ltd.,
Clapham, via Lancaster, LA2 8EB

First published 1981

© Peter R. Rodgers 1981

ISBN: 0 85206 628 7

To Jennifer, Lucy and David

Printed by Waddington & Sons (Printers) Ltd.,
Fielden Square, Rochdale Road, Todmorden, Lancs.

Contents

Cover photograph of Blue John jewellery by courtesy of the Blue John Gem Box, Matlock Bath.

ACKNOWLEDGEMENT

I would like to thank all the people who have helped in the preparation of this book. In particular I would like to thank Mr. M. Brewster, Mrs. L. Lee, Mr. and Mrs. I. Mathews, Mr. T. H. Riley; and Mr. G. Wolfendale for the photographs of jet, Blue John and black marble.

My thanks also go to Mrs. Jean Moralee for allowing specimens of Victorian jet jewellery from her excellent collection to be photographed for use in the book.

Finally my thanks must once again be extended to my family whose help and support I greatly appreciate.

P.R.R., March 1979

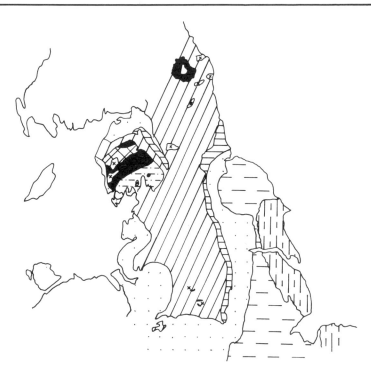

GEOLOGY OF NORTHERN ENGLAND

SEDIMENTARY ROCKS

Rocks of Cretaceous Age including clay, greensand and chalk.

Rocks of Jurassic Age including limestone, clay, marl, sandstone and shale.

Rocks of Triassic Age including marls, evaporites, pebble beds and sandstones.

Rocks of Permian Age including sandstone, marl and limestone.

Rocks of Carboniferous Age including limestone, sandstone, shale and coal.

 Rocks of Silurian Age including limestone, mudstone, siltstones and shale.

 Rocks of Ordovician Age including shale, mudstone and limestone.

IGNEOUS ROCKS

 Intrusive rocks which include granite and dolerite.

 Volcanic rocks which include basalt and andesite.

4

Preface

THE North of England is not an area renowned for things of beauty. Mention of the name conjures up thoughts of cooling towers, chimneys and large factories; in short industry and industrial dirt. To many people in Britain, the North of England is nothing more than the industrial heart of the country. It is an area to drive through on your way somewhere else, an obstacle to be overcome.

To some extent this attitude is excusable, when one considers how Britain's motorway system understandably, and thankfully, clings to the industrial centres. To anyone 'driving through' the area, such places as the Peak District, the Yorkshire Dales, and the Northumberland National Park may be on another planet. Not for one moment am I suggesting that the motorways should be pushed into areas of beauty, that would be sacrilege, but the fact remains that to many potential visitors, we are not putting on our most attractive face.

It may seem strange but gemstones are often to be found where the scenery is at its most striking and the North of England is no exception to this general rule. In the Peak District, the Lake District, the Cheviot Hills and even the Yorkshire Dales nature has provided attractive stones, many of which at one time or another man has utilized for ornamental purposes. A small number of the stones have provided the basis for successful tourist businesses in the North of England, but by far the greater majority of the gemstones in the area have never done more than provide pleasure to the small proportion of the population who know they are there.

Collecting semi-precious stones has become an increasingly popular hobby in Britain and this has been allied to the stone polishing craft called lapidary. Gemstones need to be worked. Their true beauty and character can only be properly appreciated when they have been ground and polished. Only then, when all their imperfections have been removed, are they really gemstones. Nature has done much, but it takes man's craftsmanship to bring nature's work to fruition.

The rocks which make up the British Isles are almost infinite in their variety and a good many of the earth's minerals and gemstones occur within them. Unfortunately only rarely do the gemstones achieve the usable quality which the lapidary requires. The geology of the North of England only serves to confirm this fact. But at least as far as gemstones are concerned, few areas of Britain can offer greater variety. Whether you have found, purchased or inherited one of these gemstones, you are the owner of a small part of

Britain's gemstone wealth, a wealth which is by no means excessive.

The gemstones of Northern England are very varied in character. Some are common, others are scarce. A few have earned fame, while others have never risen from obscurity. In this book I have endeavoured to outline the stones and their stories. It is millions of years since many of them were created, but still they can be found on our northern hillsides and beaches. They are a small but fascinating part of our heritage which we can all enjoy.

Mohs' Scale of Hardness

1 talc

2 gypsum
——————— 2½ finger nail
3 calcite

4 fluorite ——————— 4 copper coin

5 apatite
——————— 5½ penknife blade
6 Feldspar
——————— 6½ steel file
7 quartz

8 topaz

9 corundum

10 diamond

1.

Introducing Gemstones and Geology

GEMSTONES

WHAT is a gemstone? This is a simple enough question but when viewed in the context of Northern England, the answer must be carefully phrased.

A gemstone is defined as a mineral, usually scarce or rare, which has decorative qualities, either in its native form or when subjected to the polishing and shaping skills of a lapidary. The rarity of the gemstone is an ambiguous factor because many gemstones are comparatively common, while others may occur at only one or two locations throughout the world. Obviously, therefore, the name gemstone may cover any gem material from the exotic diamond or emerald, to the rather more lowly jasper or jade, as long as it exhibits attractive qualities.

The hardness of the gemstone is immaterial, although for durability, the harder the stone the better. Soft stones have only limited appeal because they may very easily be damaged by coming into contact with ordinary household objects.

Apart from accidents, when items of jewellery are scratched, chipped or otherwise damaged by contact with a hard object, the worst enemy of a soft gemstone is dust. Quartz is a prominent constituent of dust and is a very hard mineral indeed. A file made from the hardest and toughest alloy steel will not mark a piece of quartz, in fact the reverse will happen, the file will be abraded by the stone and lose its cutting edge. It is unfortunate that, without exception, the commercially viable gemstones of Northern England are softer than quartz and can therefore be readily abraded by dust.

All gemstones and minerals can be related to Mohs' Scale of Hardness which is an aid to identifying a stone and assessing its suitability for use in jewellery. The scale covers ten points from talc at 1 on the scale to diamond at 10. A number of household items can be related to the scale for comparison purposes. (See opposite.)

Taken to its logical conclusion calcite at 3 on the scale will scratch gypsum and talc, but can be scratched by fluorite and all the harder minerals. A steel file will scratch feldspar, apatite, and fluorite, etcetera, but will itself be abraded by quartz, topaz, corundum and diamond.

Mohs' Scale does not offer a precise hardness measurement, indeed the difference in hardness between fluorite and apatite, 4 and 5 respectively, is not the same as the difference between corundum and diamond at 9 and 10. However, other minerals can

7

be compared with those on Mohs' Scale and a guide to their comparative hardness established.

Stones which occur above 6½ on the scale are most suitable for jewellery purposes, but softer stones may still be suitable if treated with care by the wearer.

Having outlined the qualities necessary in a gemstone, it is important to relate these qualities to the stones which form the basis of this book. Unfortunately it is here that we will experience many surprises.

The minerals which have been used commercially as the basis for successful businesses are few, and without exception are soft stones when compared to Mohs' Scale. Blue John as a form of fluorite is placed at 4 on the hardness scale. Jet, which is really a form of the rock lignite, is rated between 3 and 4 while hematite, which can tend to vary in hardness, is usually rated around 6 on the scale. Obviously none of these stones is ideal for the purpose for which it is used.

The North of England is not devoid of the harder gemstones but these have rarely been worked commercially, although their presence has enabled local amateur lapidary enthusiasts many opportunities to enjoy a profitable hobby. These stones which include the quartz varieties, agate and carnelian, are hard enough to be highly suitable for jewellery purposes when attractive examples are found.

Many decorative rocks, chiefly limestones, which occur in the North of England have been utilized for a wide variety of ornamental purposes, ranging from table tops and fireplaces to jewellery and gravestones. During the 19th century, a large industry became established, working limestones that were exposed in the Pennines. The limestones which were known locally as marbles were relatively hard but brittle, and items manufactured from them were unable to withstand knocks. This fact ultimately led to the downfall of the industry.

The Lake District slate which enjoys a wide market today suffers from similar problems to the limestones but is not as brittle. For ornamental objects it is satisfactory, but should it be manufactured into items which receive everyday use, it would be most unsuitable.

Precious and Semi-Precious Stones

The terms precious and semi-precious stones apply to gemstones and can create confusion in the mind of the reader. There are no precious stones to be found in any part of Britain, let alone the North of England. Blue John, which is possibly the rarest gemstone in the area, would only be rated as semi-precious. Rarity is a factor in deciding whether a stone is precious or semi-precious, but the suitability of the stone for use in jewellery is also an important consideration.

The many small agates and other gemstones which occur on beaches in our area belong to the semi-precious stone category.

8

However, the size and quality in which they occur only rarely makes them suitable for jewellery and consequently many of the local specimens are not semi-precious stones.

The fact that gemstones are expected to exhibit a reasonable hardness is inescapable but, in the case of commercially viable gemstones from the North of England, this factor is overcome because the stones are indigenous. In short they have local appeal and outside their immediate area their sales potential is much reduced.

None of the gemstones which occur in the North of England offer the sparkle, fire or transparency which would qualify them for the term precious stones. Much of their appeal is founded upon the high lustre they can obtain when polished by a lapidary. However, they all have qualities which are not exhibited by the vast majority of minerals and in their own way are undoubtedly gemstones.

GEOLOGY

Gemstones are usually varieties of minerals, or occasionally rocks, and as such their occurrence can to a large extent be predicted by anyone with a little knowledge of geology and mineralogy. The serious collector of minerals and gemstones soon learns to understand the relationships which exist between the main types of rock and the minerals that may be associated with them.

Minerals and Rocks

Minerals are chemical elements or compounds which occur naturally within the earth's crust. They have a definite composition or range of compositions. They are formed in cracks, fissures and other cavities in rocks.

Rocks are mixtures of minerals and may have been created by any one of three basic processes. Igneous rocks are formed as a result of molten rock (magma) rising from within the earth. Intrusive igneous rocks solidify slowly beneath the earth's surface and give rise to colourful rocks like granite. Volcanoes also produce igneous rocks which are called extrusive as they solidify on the earth's surface in contact with the atmosphere. Many mineral veins are formed as a late stage in the cooling of intrusive igneous rocks. Gemstones may also be formed in volcanic rocks due to hydrothermal[1] activity.

Metamorphic rocks are created when existing rocks of any type are subjected to great heat and pressure under the surface of the earth. The existing rock is completely re-crystallized into a new rock. Some gemstones are formed by metamorphism including garnet and kyanite. Serpentine is a gemstone, but may be formed by the metamorphism of a basic igneous rock. Serpentine is a decorative stone which is rock rather than mineral.

1. Hydrothermal is the name given to a process whereby heated water brings about changes in the earth's crust.

Sedimentary rocks are formed by the accumulation of debris, either under the sea or in desert conditions. The sediments are subsequently compacted into stone. They are aggregates derived from the erosion of existing rocks. Minerals and gemstones are rarely to be found with them, but there is one exception. Limestone, which is a sedimentary rock, is very soluble in mineralizing fluids and this has encouraged the formation of mineral veins in limestone. The mineralizing fluids still originate from an igneous body within the earth's crust, but are very willingly accommodated by the limestone. Other sedimentary rocks such as shale, being less soluble, will often restrict the passage of mineralizing fluids and bottle them up in the rocks below.

Rock and Mineral Relationships

Certain rocks and minerals may frequently be found together and this is a clue not only to the identity of a mineral, but also an indication as to where to look for it. A good example is given by limestone which is an impure form of calcium carbonate. Calcite which is pure calcium carbonate is, not surprisingly, the mineral most likely to be encountered in cracks and fissures in limestone.

Silica is a common find as quartz veins in igneous and metamorphic rocks, which may also contain quartz as an integral mineral. Quartz, in veins or cavities, is somewhat less common in lime rich sediments and the more basic igneous rocks. The silica gemstones are fairly predictable by the rock company they keep. The chalcedony group, namely agate and carnelian, are to be expected in intermediate or slightly acid volcanic rocks. The coarsely crystalline gemstones such as amethyst and smoky quartz also occur here but, unlike the chalcedony group, also occur in intrusive igneous rocks such as granite.

Olivine and minerals of the zeolite group favour the basic volcanic rock and their presence will almost certainly rule out the possibility of quartz being present in any quantity. The only 'rocks' which transgress these relationships are glacial deposits where rock debris from many different areas of the country have been accumulated together. Such deposits are easily identified for what they are and present no real complication. However, they can provide an unexpected array of gemstones and as such their story will be dealt with in another chapter.

The Geological Time Scale

In order that the story of the gemstones of Northern England can be fully explained, it is necessary on occasions to refer to the Geological Time Scale. This scale was developed by geologists as an aid to dating rocks and geological history since the creation of the planet earth.

Our earth was created around 4,500 million years ago and although geologists have recounted the earth's early history, there is little evidence to be found in the remains of the rocks formed over 600 million years ago. Indeed our knowledge of the happenings on earth during the last 600 million years is infinitely greater than our knowledge of events during the previous 4,000 million years. The reason is that the early rocks have been largely removed from the face of the earth by more recent geological events. The younger rocks have been preserved and carry the information of recent geological upheavals in great detail.

The geology of the North of England is based primarily on rocks of Carboniferous Age or older. The Lake District is hewn out of rocks of Silurian Age; the Cheviot Hills belong to the Devonian Period and the Pennines are Carboniferous; only on the east coast shall we encounter younger rocks.

Eras	Period	Epoch	Millions of years since start of period
CAINOZOIC	QUATERNARY	Recent (Holocene) Pleistocene	2
	TERTIARY	Pliocene	12
		Miocene	25
		Oligocene	40
		Eocene	60
		Paleocene	65
MESOZOIC	CRETACEOUS		135
	JURASSIC		181
	TRIASSIC		230
PALAEOZOIC	PERMIAN		280
	CARBONIFEROUS	Coal Measure Times Millstone Grit Times Carboniferous Limestone Times	350
	OLD RED SANDSTONE (DEVONIAN)		410
	SILURIAN		440
	ORDOVICIAN		500
	CAMBRIAN		600
	PRECAMBRIAN		Undefined
	ORIGIN OF THE EARTH		Over 4,500 million years ago

2. Gemstones of the Cheviot Hills

THE Cheviot Hills dominate the scenery of north east England and south east Scotland. They form the high ground along the eastern end of the Scottish Border, but lie primarily on the English side. For countless centuries the hills have formed a natural barrier to man's movement to north or south. Even the Romans, in the second century, found difficulty in overcoming this barrier, although their situation was of course not helped by the Caledonians who fought the legions tooth and nail, doubtless using their knowledge of this hilly border country to considerable advantage. However, the origin of the Cheviot Hills goes back much further in time.

The Cheviot Hills started life around 400 million years ago as one of a number of volcanoes which were active in Britain at the time. Most of the volcanic activity was taking place in central Scotland around what are now the cities of Glasgow and Edinburgh. Great quantities of volcanic rocks were to be formed during this period of vulcanism which lasted several million years, in the time known to geologists as the Lower Devonian.

It is generally considered that the first stages in the growth of the Cheviot volcano were extremely explosive and huge quantities of hot ash were blasted into the sky, to fall as red hot rain over the surface of the surrounding hills. The confirmation of this explosive phase is to be found in the agglomerates[1] and ashes which are known today overlying the folded and greatly eroded Silurian rocks on which the volcanic rocks lie.

At this time Northern England formed the foothills on the fringe of a huge mountain chain which existed to the north. These mountains which are today known as the Caledonian Mountains extended from Ireland, through Scotland to Norway and probably ranked alongside the Himalayas for enormity. The Cheviot volcano was a product of the creation of this mountain chain.

When the explosive ash cycle was over, great outpourings of molten lava took place. The lava flowing out over the surrounding countryside was to build up to a very considerable depth before the volcano became extinct. How many times the volcano exploded into violence has never been established, but we can assume from the quantity of lava accumulated that it was active over a long period of time.

Later, when the volcanic activity had died down, a large mass of molten rock (magma) was pushed upwards into the core of the old

---

1. Agglomerates are Pyroclastic rocks consisting mainly of fragments larger than 2 centimetres in diameter.

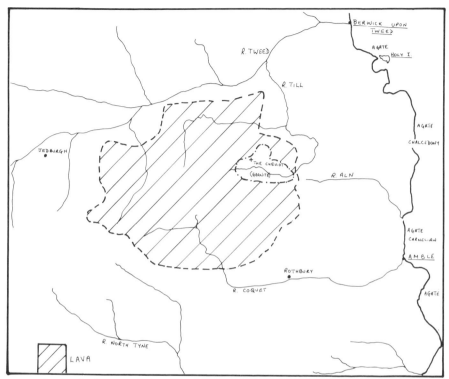

Geological map of the Cheviot Hills, also indicating distribution of gemstones along the Northumberland coast.

volcano. This igneous intrusion cooled slowly, surrounded as it was by older rocks, and eventually solidified as granite. This phase of the igneous activity was terminated by the intrusion of a number of dykes which dissect both granite and lava.

Subsequently the granite has undergone quite extensive modification in places which can be attributed to hydrothermal processes and pneumatolysis[1]. The lavas have been similarly affected by the hydrothermal processes and in some places are considerably altered. Tourmalinisation, which is a type of pneumatolysis, has taken place in the Cheviot granite. However crystals of green tourmaline, while present, are extremely small.

Since the end of this volcanic episode, around 400 million years ago, the area has suffered subsidence, uplift and erosion on several occasions. Consequently the volcano and its now ancient products are much less complete than they once were. However, over 20

1. Pneumatolysis is the name given to changes brought about by the action of hot gaseous substances (other than water) associated with igneous activity.

13

square miles of lava are still covering the Cheviot area despite the efforts of erosion. It is possible that the volcanic rocks once covered a far greater area than we realise today, having been subjected to considerable erosion. However it is also possible that the lavas still exist beneath the younger sedimentary rocks of the northern Pennines which occur to the south.

The granite forms a dome-like structure in the heart of the lava, but is only exposed over a relatively small area. The original upper surface of the granite intrusion and the upper surface of the exposed granite today, are in some places synonymous. Indeed at one or two locations remnants of the lava which formed the roof of the intrusion can still be found, although it has been subjected to considerable modification (metamorphism) due to the heat from the molten granite. The highest point in the Cheviot Hills is the Cheviot itself which is hewn out of granite and falls on the English side of the Scottish Border.

The scenery we enjoy in the Cheviot Hills today is to some extent due to the effects of glacial ice during the Pleistocene Ice Age. The last glaciation came to an end around 10,000 years ago, but not before much of the British Isles had undergone significant modification. The Cheviot Hills, being high ground, became a centre for glaciation while at the same time they were an obstacle to the ice flowing from the north and west. As far as can be established, the Cheviots were never overcome by ice from the north or west although the Cheviot ice itself was deflected eastwards towards our present east coast and then southwards due to the influence of Scandinavian ice approaching from the east. Large quantities of rock debris were collected under the moving ice, and as the ice moved southwards, were transported out of the area. This characteristic of the ice movement was not peculiar to the Cheviot Hills, but happened over the entire glaciated area of Britain. The result was that large masses of pebbles and rock debris from the northern hills were distributed over different areas of the country. The fact that rock debris from the Cheviot Hills was carried southwards, along what is now the east coast of England, will be of considerable importance later in the book.

Most of the existing soil was removed by the glaciers, but during the last 10,000 years soil has again been created and an enticing coat of greenery now covers much of the Cheviot Hills. Soil derived from igneous rocks tends to be very fertile, so it is hardly surprising that rock exposures are very scarce. The main exception to this is provided by the many rivers which rise in the Cheviots and have carved a path through them, exposing and eroding the rocks over which they pass.

Today the Cheviots form an excitingly beautiful area of Northern England and are the basis of the Northumberland National Park. To the north, in Scotland, the Cheviots give way to somewhat lower land carved out of Old Red Sandstone sedimentary rocks, while the lowland to the east and the Pennines to the south are made of

Carboniferous sediments, which include limestone, sandstone and coal. Neither the red desert sandstones of the Borders nor the rugged delta sandstones of the Pennines, can offer the beauty to be found among the rolling rounded symmetry of the volcanic Cheviot Hills.

Agate, Chalcedony and the Quartz Gemstones

The lavas of the Cheviot Hills are primarily andesites[1] and are commonly vesicular which means they exhibit the shapes of gas bubbles which existed in the molten rock. These cavities called vesicals are usually empty unless hydrothermal activity has taken place. Hydrothermal activity can result in the vesicals being infilled with other minerals including gemstones.

Hydrothermal activity quite frequently takes place in areas where volcanoes have been active. The process is dependent upon the presence of hot water or superheated steam which is created close to an igneous body. The hot liquid which percolates through the rock structure of the earth's crust dissolves minerals out of the rocks as it goes. Silica, a mixture of silicon and oxygen, is one of the minerals which may be dissolved in this way and silica is a mineral which may exist in a number of gemstone forms.

Hot liquids rise and so the hot silica rich liquid rises upwards through the overlying rocks, cooling as it goes. As it cools, so the minerals it has dissolved are deposited in any cracks, fissures or vesicals in the area. When silica is deposited in vesicals in lavas in this manner, a wide selection of products may be the result on cooling.

The most likely form the newly deposited silica may take is quartz. This is a coarsely crystalline form of silica and is usually colourless and uninteresting. However the gemstone forms may also occur, these being amethyst which is purple, smoky quartz which is brown, citrine which is yellow/lemon and morion the black variety. All are coarsely crystalline quartz gemstones.

A relatively slow rate of cooling could lead to the formation of the quartz gemstones. Faster cooling, combined with a number of critical chemical reactions, may result in the formation of the crypto or micro crystalline quartz varieties which are known under the general name chalcedony. Chalcedony is deposited as a gel which may be alkaline in nature; being alkaline it may react with iron in the surrounding rock to create a coloured precipitate which forms around the edge of the gel. When, and if, the precipitate diffuses inward towards the centre, further reactions may take place which result in the building up of a multi-banded pattern in the gel. On hardening the gel becomes a special type of chalcedony known as agate. There is an infinite range of patterns that may exist in the agates, but generally they are concentric to the shape of the vesicals (gas bubbles) in which they have been formed. Agates may be

1. Andesites are lavas composed of a silicate of alumina, lime and soda.

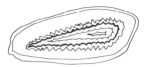  **Patterns to be found in agates.**

multi-coloured, depending on the amount of impurities, usually iron, present within each band of precipitate.

Other varieties of chalcedony occur, colour being the prime variant. These are not usually banded, although banding can frequently be observed within chalcedony of a uniform colour. Orange chalcedony is known as carnelian, while the grey variety which is exceedingly common is simply known as common chalcedony. Chrysoprase and plasma are green varieties and bloodstone is green with red spots; sard on the other hand is red. Onyx and sard onyx are straight banded forms of agate. Chrysoprase, plasma, bloodstone and onyx are not to be found in the Cheviot Hills.

Jasper is another form of silica which can also occur and is often red, although brown, yellow and green varieties are not uncommon. Jasper is not translucent like chalcedony or transparent like the quartz gemstones but opaque. Its colourings are again due to impurities within the stone.

The volcanic rocks of the Cheviots were subjected to extensive hydrothermal activity and this in turn resulted in the formation of a number of silica gemstones in the vesicals of the lavas. Quartz in its colourless crystalline form is common throughout the Cheviot lavas. Chalcedony is equally abundant in its grey common form and is joined by the orange variety called carnelian. Some sard occurs but is relatively scarce.

Pride of place in the Cheviots undoubtedly belongs to agate for in the Cheviot Hills, agates are not only at their most colourful, they are also reasonably common. The only unfortunate fact is that usually they are small when compared with specimens from other parts of Britain. However, as always there are exceptions and indeed one or two quite large examples have been found. Specimens up to 5 centimetres in diameter are normally to be expected.

Agates may on occasion have crystalline quartz centres and it is here that amethyst or smoky quartz may be found. Other examples may have hollow centres, the inside walls being lined with crystals all pointing inwards. These are called geodes and are usually to be found where the agates occur. The crystals they contain will be amethyst, smoky quartz, rock crystal or milky quartz. However the crystals may be very small.

Other minerals may sometimes occur alongside the gemstones and they too owe their origin to either the hydrothermal processes or weathering. Calcite is an occasional find as is chlorite — which is a common mineral in rocks which have been modified by hydrothermal activity, and wad — which is a manganese mineral. Manganese dioxide, which is the chemical name for wad, is sometimes found in the most beautiful dendrite[1] patterns on the rock surfaces, but even in this form it is not a gemstone by any interpretation.

Quite obviously gemstones, usually of the silica family, are fairly common within the andesitic lavas of the Cheviot Hills. However knowing they are there is one thing, finding them is quite another.

Gemstone Locations in the Cheviot Hills

The Cheviot Hills offer very few rock exposures and consequently it is the streams and river banks that offer the best opportunity to explore the bed rock. A quick look at the map reveals that a number of rivers rise in the Cheviots, and that in several instances the rivers are mirrored by roads which climb up the same river valleys. Access to the hills is therefore fairly easy.

Bearing in mind that the Cheviot Hills cover a large area of country, it is necessary to use more than one centre if the hills are to be adequately explored. Good centres include Rothbury, for the southern Cheviots, and Wooler for the hills nearest to the Scottish Border.

Southern Cheviots

The volcanic rock is best displayed in the southern area of the Cheviot Hills, the rounded lava hills realizing a barren beauty they seldom achieve in the north. It is the River Coquet which has dissected the hills in this southern area and a road runs alongside the river almost to its source. The road, however, also leads to the Redesdale Ministry of Defence Range situated high in the hills and its presence does much to overshadow the beauty of the countryside. One soon becomes familiar with the frequent signs and red flags which mean that the army is practising and the presence of the general public is not to be tolerated in certain areas. One supposes that target practice is essential, but why is it always the most beautiful areas that suffer? And don't forget this area is part of the Northumberland National Park.

The River Coquet rises in the south western corner of the Cheviot Hills and flows through the volcanic rocks for almost 20 miles before it reaches the lower ground near Rothbury. Anyone searching for agates can do much worse than explore the various shingle banks which occur intermittently along this entire stretch of river. The agates and other gemstones occur as pebbles within the shingle. However, it must be pointed out that the pebbles are much less rounded than those you find on a beach.

It is also well worthwhile examining the shingle in the shallower parts of the river. After a hard winter, when the river has been at its most turbulent, it is often possible to see the more brightly coloured

1. Dendrite means that a stone or mineral has tree-like markings.

gemstones in the water. Of course, during the summer, most of the pebbles become moss coated and are impossible to differentiate.

Specimens of agate, chalcedony including carnelian, and jasper are the most common finds and a good place to start looking is in the river at the ford at Harbottle. Fields in this area also yield specimens. From Alwinton it is possible to follow the river into the hills, stopping to investigate promising areas of shingle as necessary. Neither should one overlook the tributaries of the Coquet for these also carry gemstone specimens.

The agates to be found in the southern Cheviots are often brightly coloured in purples and reds, but orange, blue and grey specimens also occur. Amethyst and smoky quartz crystals may be present as the crystalline centres of the agates. In fact one frequently finds purple amethyst contrasting quite fiercely with orange bands in some specimens. Waterworn agates will frequently exhibit a jelly-like appearance and broken specimens will obviously show the tell-tale banded structure. In a rock face, the agates stand out due to their rounded bubble-like appearance, resembling plums in a very hard igneous pudding. The outer skins of the agates when whole may be red, green or brown, the colouration being due to a thin film of mineral around the specimen. This mineral is created around the agates due to hydrothermal alteration of the volcanic rock.

In the higher region of the river, it is well worth searching drainage ditches which have been cut on the hillsides. Also newly cut tracks over the hills may yield gemstones. Providing the red flags are not flying, it is often worth taking a walk over the hills, examining rock exposures as and when you come upon them. This is the most rewarding approach to finding gemstones. It is surprising what you stumble upon and at the same time you can enjoy the Cheviot scenery at its best.

Access to the granite area of the Cheviots is most easily obtained by taking the minor road to the village of Lynhope. A short walk to Lynhope Spout, the attractive waterfall, leads on to the granite but within the granite, gemstones are extremely scarce. Only tourmaline is a possibility, but when it occurs the crystals are so minute that they do not have any gemstone application. Quartz is fairly common in veins in the granite and crystals also occur. Unfortunately the crystals are usually of milky quartz and not amethyst or smoky quartz, the gemstones. The Lynhope Burn joins the River Breamish at Lynhope and from here towards the east, agate and chalcedony pebbles may be found among the river gravel.

Northern Cheviots

A large part of the Cheviot Hills falls to the north of the Scottish Border and as such are outside the scope of this book. However, for completeness it is necessary to point out that agate and jasper have been found near Jedburgh in the Scottish Cheviots.

The north east corner of these volcanic hills is easily accessible from the town of Wooler. From here it is possible to drive up the valleys into the Cheviots towards Langlee and Langleeford. The road runs parallel with Harthope Burn which is an interesting source of gemstones. These may include agate, chalcedony, amethyst and smoky quartz.

One burn near Langleeford flows along the crush zone between the granite and lava areas and was once known as Diamond Burn. Not that diamonds were ever found here, but there was once a surfeit of small clear colourless quartz crystals which were reminiscent of the precious stone. The burn still yields quartz crystals as well as crystals of amethyst and smoky quartz. The quartz boulders, which occasionally yield the crystal lined pockets, may also exhibit the small green tourmaline crystals previously mentioned. Some chalcedony and agate also occurs here, but are not in the amygdale[1] form in which they occur in the lavas of the southern Cheviots. Instead they occur as small areas within the quartz boulders. Other minerals in this area are calcite, pyrolusite, hematite and goethite, but none of these are gemstones.

Streams which flow along crush zones between the granite and lava areas of the Cheviots are frequently known to expose rocks which may contain gemstones. Quite a number of appropriate streams exist, but few are easily accessible.

Fields around the eastern side of the Cheviot Hills may also yield examples of Cheviot gemstones. The specimens may have been carried to their present site by glacial action or by water from the melting ice. Of course fields can only be prospected with the farmer's permission and this will not be given when the crops are high. The best time for field work is in the early spring, before seeding commences, or the late autumn when the crops have been harvested.

Several gravel pits working fluvio-glacial deposits also exist in the Wooler district and agates may frequently be found amongst the glacial outwash deposits. The banks of the River Tweed near Wark also yield specimens of agate and chalcedony as do a number of fields near the same village.

The gemstones which adorn the Cheviot Hills have never been used for jewellery or ornamental purposes other than on an amateur scale. This is due to the fact that the gemstones that occur are quite difficult to find and very mixed in quality. But this is not the end of the story. Indeed it must be said that for colour and interest, the agates of the Cheviot Hills are second to none and can on occasions readily rank alongside the most exotic specimens from anywhere in the world.

1. Amygdale form means almond shaped.

3. Gemstones of the East Coast

FOR the purposes of this book I will review the coast of England from the Scottish Border to The Wash. This includes the coastline of Northumberland, Durham, Yorkshire and Humberside, and Lincolnshire. In order to consider the gemstones which occur on the east coast, we must consider the origins of the many types of pebbles which occur amongst the shingle.

The first obvious source of beach pebbles is the cliffs adjacent to the beach. Twice every day the waves ascend the beach and assault the cliffs. In the summer when the seas are calm, comparatively little damage is done to the cliffs, but in the winter time when stormy seas pound away at the cliff faces, erosion can take place fairly rapidly. Small fragments of rock break off and are washed out amongst the shingle, where the pebble forming process begins.

Obviously all the rocks which form cliffs on our east coast will contribute pebbles to the beach and any minerals or gemstones the cliffs contain will be eroded out into the shingle. Our next task is to consider the geology of the cliffs which make up the north-east coast of England.

Starting at the Scottish Border and working southwards, the first type of rock we encounter is limestone of Carboniferous Age. This is the famous 'Mountain Limestone' but in many places on this stretch of coast, the rocks are completely hidden beneath the sand dunes and other deposits. Virtually the first hard rock to be seen is the igneous intrusion upon which the castle of Holy Island stands. A little further south the Whin Sill, another igneous intrusion, outcrops in a similar situation beneath Bamburgh Castle.

The limestone continues southwards and is eventually superseded by first the Whin Sill and then by rocks of the Millstone Grit Series which extend southwards to Alnmouth. Rocks of the Coal Measures take over on the coast near Amble and extend southwards along Druridge Bay, where the fossilised remains of a coal forest are occasionally exposed at extremely low tides.

Rocks of the Coal Measures which include sandstones, shales and coal extend southward to the River Tyne, where limestone of Permian Age takes over. This limestone is only succeeded by sandstone a few miles north of the mouth of the River Tees.

Once south of the River Tees, the cliff scenery is hewn out of Jurassic rocks primarily limestones, sandstones and shales. The shales are particularly noticeable around Sandsend, Whitby and Robin Hood's Bay while the sandstones are prominent in the Castle Hill at Scarborough. The coastline from Redcar to south of Flamborough Head is backed almost entirely by cliffs and offers some

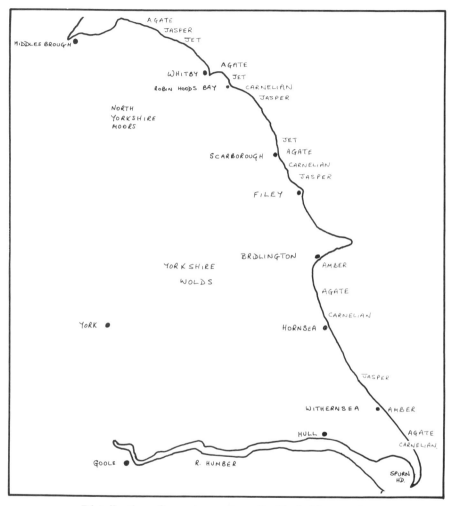

Distribution of gemstones along the Yorkshire coast.

very beautiful scenery.

South of Filey the famous chalk rock comes to the fore and continues southwards beyond the Humber to the mouth of the Wash. Around Flamborough Head the chalk forms cliffs, but on nearing Bridlington they disappear and from here onwards such cliffs as occur are not composed of solid rock.

Each of the rocks which occur on the coastline may be found as pebbles on beaches in the neighbourhood and, due to other processes I will describe later in the chapter, they may also be found further afield. However, softer rocks will soon be eroded by the tide and examples will not travel far from their point of origin.

Cliffs form a ready source of beach material, but rivers may also contribute pebbles to the beaches. And in this case the pebbles may have originated many miles away inland. As far as the north-east coast of England is concerned, few of the rivers are likely to carry gemstones to the sea. For the most part the rivers in question rise in the Pennines which are composed of the same Carboniferous limestones, sandstones and Coal Measures which are exposed on the Northumberland coast.

The Rivers Breamish, Till, Coquet, Tyne and Tweed which rise in the Cheviot Hills are, however, a potential source of gemstones. The gemstones in question being those which occur in the volcanic rocks and which we have already considered. As a result, it is not unusual to find pebbles of the volcanic rocks and the Cheviot granite on the east coast beaches.

The cliffs on our coast and the rivers are the main source of new pebble materials on to the beaches, but there are two other processes which can have some effect. The first is a major supplier of pebbles and is, in fact, responsible for the vast majority of the gemstones on the east coast. To find the origin of this source of pebbles, we have to turn back the clock once again to the Great Ice Age.

As we have already seen the Ice Age began around one million years ago and the last glaciation came to an end approximately 10,000 years ago. During this period of time the ice advanced southwards over Britain on no fewer than four occasions. Each glaciation began with a cooling of the climate, when the winter snows lingered into summer and a slow build up of snow began on our mountains. Eventually the snow was compacted into glacier ice and the glaciers were drawn off our northern mountains to spread their icy fingers over the British scene.

The ice sheets were very destructive and their effect on the landscape was quite considerable. They broke rocks away from existing rock faces. They also cleared away most of the soil and rocks off the rock surfaces over which they passed. Slowly they advanced out over the countryside, generally in a southward direction. As they proceeded so the rock debris they had collected travelled with them, away from the area where they were originally created.

Ultimately the ice reached a point on its journey southwards where the temperature was too warm for it to exist, and here its forward motion ceased. Eventually, with the onset of warmer conditions the ice melted. This resulted in great columns of water flowing out from under the ice. The water carried the large quantities of rock debris with it and deposited it over the surrounding country. In some cases the rock debris was simply left behind as a monument to the passing of the ice. The resulting debris is called boulder clay.

Boulder clay lives up to its name. It consists of a dark brown or grey clay with numerous pebbles protruding from it. In some places on our east coast, the clay is present as low cliffs which sit upon the harder bed rock. Cliffs of this type are especially common in Yorkshire: around Whitby where they can sometimes be seen overlying the Jurassic shales, south of Scarborough, and on the long stretch of coast from Bridlington to Spurn Point. The Lincolnshire coast also exhibits boulder clay cliffs, and clay may be found on the Northumberland coast.

Although the clay is highly tenacious, particularly in the way it clings to your wellingtons, it is easily eroded by the sea. Naturally enough this erosion only serves to release the pebbles it contains on to the beach, where the tide hastily shuffles them amongst the other pebbles.

We have now seen a process where pebbles and rock fragments collected on hills in the north, have been transported towards the south and abandoned. The tide has then washed these pebbles out on to the nearby beach, in many cases hundreds of miles from their places of origin.

Our knowledge of ice movement during the last glaciation is reasonably complete, but the overall picture is still confusing. The boulder clay on the east coast was mainly derived from the north and west, but there is also an accumulation of debris from ice of Scandinavian origin.

To picture the events of this time, we must imagine ice from the highlands of Scotland pressing southwards, but being deflected eastwards by ice from the Scottish Borders and by the presence of the Cheviot Hills. Ice from south-west Scotland and the Lake District was deflected eastwards between the Cheviots and the Pennines. More Lake District ice was allowed to pass eastwards between the Durham and Yorkshire Pennines and under normal circumstances the progression would have been still further east.

Unfortunately the situation was complicated by the presence of a huge wall of Scandinavian ice which was moving to the west and was close to the position of our present east coast. One layer of ice or another may have overcome the obstacle and continued on its way, but the overall effect was to deflect the British ice southwards along what is now the coast.

The boulder clay on our east coast today must be of diverse character because pebbles of Lake District, Scottish, Cheviot and Scandinavian origin may all be found on the beaches. These findings are based upon the positive identification of rocks of specific types which are now known from other locations.

It would be surprising if amongst all the glacial debris which occurs on our coastline, there were not a few gemstones to be found. In fact due to the presence of boulder clay containing Cheviot debris, we are able to find specimens of many attractive gemstones on beaches which are, in many cases, hundreds of miles from the place where they were created.

Longshore Drift

Pebbles and rock fragments may arrive on the beach from many different sources but whatever shape they are, it is only here that the pebble forming process really begins. All the pebbles are repeatedly moved back and forth by the tide grinding them against each other, slowly eroding them into a smoother rounder shape. Large rock fragments are eroded more quickly than small ones, but the process continues regardless.

Most of the pebbles have travelled many miles before arriving on the beach, but even at this stage the journey is unfinished because all the pebbles on the beach are on the move. This process is called longshore drift.

The movement of pebbles by longshore drift is a long established process and is controlled by the combined effect of two forces, the wind and the sea. The pebbles' direction of movement may be somewhat erratic, but the overall trend is dependent upon the prevailing wind. On Britain's east coast the prevailing wind is from the north-east, consequently the pebbles on the beach move slowly southwards.

The actual process of longshore drift can be watched on the beach by anyone who takes the time and trouble. In the summer months the process is less vigorous, but it still goes on regardless. Every time a wave breaks on the shore, it moves up the beach carrying pebbles and shingle with it. However, waves do not approach the shore at right angles, but approach at an angle dictated by the wind. If the wind is blowing out of the north-east, then the waves will approach the beach from the same direction. The waves break and carry shingle up the beach in the same direction in which they are moving, that is towards the north-west.

The forward motion of the waves ceases and the backwash sets in. However, the backwash, which also moves the pebbles, is drawn straight down the beach by the effect of gravity and is not influenced by the wind. The pebbles are carried down until the next wave arrives and takes them back up the beach in the direction dictated by the wind.

This process has the effect of moving the shingle in a zig-zag motion along the beach in the direction dictated by the prevailing wind. The finer particles of shingle will move quite quickly, but the larger pebbles will only be moved regularly during the winter time when the seas are at their most violent.

Man has frequently attempted to provide stability to the beach by erecting groynes which hold back the shingle. These timber structures can frequently be seen on beaches at holiday resorts on the east coast. Headlands and narrow bays will tend to hold back the movement of shingle, but over a long period of time these obstacles are overcome.

Of course on occasions when the wind is from the south-west the pebbles will tend to reverse their path, but this will only slow down

24

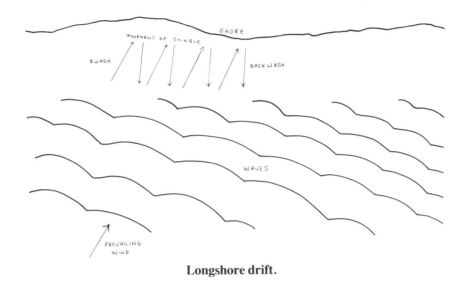

Longshore drift.

the general southerly trend. An area of coast also exists in Norfolk where the north-easterly winds encourage the pebbles to move not southwards, but west towards the Wash. This is entirely due to the geography of the coastline.

Longshore drift has, over a period of thousands of years, re-distributed the shingle. Pebbles from the boulder clay, pebbles carried down rivers, even pebbles from the beaches of Scotland have been washed into this area. If you walk on a beach on our east coast, you will see how varied the pebbles are in character. Indeed very few seem to be alike. To many people the beaches of north-east England are among the most stimulating in the country which is largely due to the cosmopolitan nature of the pebbles.

Agate, Chalcedony and Jasper

By far the most common gemstones on the east coast of England belong to the silica family. They are, in fact, all varieties of chalcedony, and do not generally include the coarsely crystalline quartz gemstones.

The chalcedony gemstones which occur on the north-east coast of England are not related in any way to the solid geology of the coastline. Undoubtedly a reasonable number of these gemstones have been carried down the rivers from the Cheviot Hills, but many more will have originated out of the boulder clay cliffs which exist along large areas of the coastline.

The boulder clay which now exists on the coast originated from many different parts of the country. Any gemstones in the clay can

25

only have originated in areas where such gemstones have been created in the parent rock. Obviously glacial deposits which include pebbles and rocks from the Cheviot Hills will contain the silica gemstones. After investigation, it is now possible to say with reasonable certainty that the vast majority of chalcedony gemstones which occur on the east coast, were originally of Cheviot origin.

Specimens of agate, carnelian and common chalcedony are the predominant varieties and these are similar in colour and patterns to those found today in the Cheviot Hills. Indeed the only other part of Britain which yields any quantity of these gemstones is central Scotland and the colours, particularly of the agates, are quite different.

There are, however, occasional exceptions to this rule. I have located a number of agates on the beaches in Yorkshire which are almost certainly not of Cheviot origin and greatly resemble specimens from the coast of Angus in Scotland. Such specimens may be derived from local boulder clay which is of Scottish origin. On the other hand, they may have been transported by the glaciers to the east coast near Berwick or Dunbar in Scotland and then washed southwards by longshore drift.

Unfortunately the distribution of glacial debris (boulder clay) along this coast is extremely confused. Ice from so many different areas was converging on our coastline that the original source of the clay at any one location is almost impossible to define. Of course the clay from one area may well overlie the clay from another, and this is particularly true when one considers that the clay cliffs may be well over 100 feet in height in some areas.

Common chalcedony, which is the grey variety, is to be found on many beaches along the east coast. Long exposure on the beach, however, may cause specimens to weather from grey to white, the white colour being usually restricted to the outer surface of the stone. In some cases the specimens may strongly resemble flint.

Carnelian, the beautiful orange form of chalcedony, is extremely common on beaches throughout the entire area. Unfortunately, it is usually only to be found as very small pieces in the smaller shingle.

Movement of ice away from the high ground during the Pleistocene Ice Age. Note the ice from Scandinavia approaching from the east.

Larger pieces, up to an inch in diameter, may occur but are relatively scarce.

Agate is perhaps the most common of the silica gemstones on this coast and there may be quite considerable overlap with common chalcedony and carnelian. Grey and white agates occur quite commonly, although the nicer specimens have a blue cast. Carnelian agates are usually orange and white banded and are easily found. Many of the small specimens of carnelian may have formed part of a carnelian agate before being broken down to their existing size.

Orange, brown, purple and red agates are the most common varieties on the east coast and may be looked upon as being of Cheviot origin. Pink and blue specimens are more typically Scottish in origin, but this is not a hard and fast rule by any means. Unlike the agates found in the Cheviot Hills, most of the gemstone pebbles are only broken pieces of larger specimens which have been smoothed by erosion.

The identification of these gemstones may be something of a problem for the uninitiated and it can take quite a long time to get your eye used to differentiating between gemstones and less exotic pebbles. The problem is further aggravated by the very varied character of pebbles to be found on the beaches in question. There are, however, a number of simple rules one can follow which will help break down the problem of identification.

The gemstones are usually brightly coloured and attractive; this fact alone puts them apart from the vast majority of beach pebbles. Agate, chalcedony and carnelian are also translucent which means that light can pass through them, while most beach pebbles are totally opaque. This facet of the gemstones' character can be put to good use by the collector. On bright sunny days on the beach, walk towards the sun. The translucent character of the gemstones makes them glow under these conditions and they can be easily identified. Another trick of the trade is to search the beach as the tide is receding. When the pebbles are wet, the gemstones stand out quite clearly from their less colourful companions.

Other points to remember: Chalcedony is a form of quartz which means it is hard (7 on Mohs' Scale), and this means that specimens may tend to remain angular even though they have been on the beach for a very long period of time. All types of chalcedony tend to exhibit a waxy lustre and may retain a jelly-like appearance when waterworn. However, perhaps the most important fact of all to remember is not to anticipate finding huge specimens. Apart from the occasional exception, specimens will rarely exceed 1½ inches in diameter.

Jasper is a different gemstone altogether, but it has undergone the same distributive action caused by the Ice Age and is consequently present in the boulder clay cliffs along the coast. As pebbles on the beach, jasper will also suffer the same fate as other pebbles with regard to longshore drift. However its origins and character-

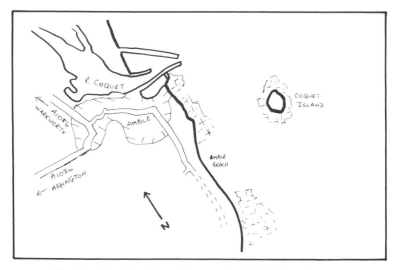

The beach at Amble at the mouth of the River Coquet.

istics are not those of the varieties of chalcedony I have already described.

Although jasper may be formed in much the same way as the chalcedony gemstones, it is also created by another process called metamorphism. This process which is usually associated with the creation of huge mountain chains can take place on a small scale around an igneous intrusion. It is the presence of heat and pressure which allows the complete modification of a rock to take place. This modification of the rock is called metamorphism.

Jasper may be formed by the metamorphism of silica rich clays and much of it may have been created in just this way. This stone is classed as a form of chalcedony, although its structure is somewhat different. It is, however, a gemstone and as far as Britain is concerned, it is a very common one.

The fact that it is common here has tended to make it considerably underrated as a gemstone. Indeed, allowing for careful choice of specimens, this is one of the few gemstones in the country which has potential commercial exploitation.

Most British jasper is red/purple although green, brown and yellow varieties occur with reasonable frequency. It is often mottled, having more than one colour in each specimen. Unlike the other chalcedony gemstones, jasper is opaque and pebbles frequently contain much porosity. When wet its pebbles show their beautiful colours off to full advantage.

Identifying jasper pebbles on a beach is no problem, although one might have difficulty believing that a semi-precious stone can be

28

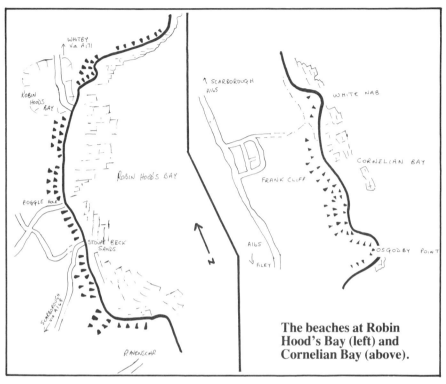

The beaches at Robin Hood's Bay (left) and Cornelian Bay (above).

quite as common as its pebbles suggest.

Another slightly confusing factor is the size of jasper pebbles. Many are of course small, but it is not at all unusual on the east coast of England to find pebbles up to 8 or 10 inches in diameter. However not even these boulders can compare with beaches in North Wales where 2 and 3 foot diameter rocks occur.

Locations

The processes of glacial drift and longshore drift have worked together to spread pebbles and rock fragments over a wide area of coastline on which they would not otherwise occur. These processes are haphazard, but their combined effect has been to distribute the more common gemstones over a long stretch of coast. The result is that most beaches on the north-east coast of England will yield specimens of agate and chalcedony if you search hard enough.

The fact that the distribution of the gemstones has been very effective over the years, does not mean that no superior locations exist. There are, in fact, a number of beaches which offer a larger concentration of gemstones than the norm and to find these, we have to consider the various points where gemstones are delivered on the beach.

Agate and chalcedony pebbles are more readily found in Northumberland on the beaches adjacent to the mouths of certain rivers. These are, in fact, the rivers which rise in the Cheviot Hills and carry fragments of the volcanic rocks and their gemstones to the east coast. The beaches south of Amble, on the Northumberland coast, benefit from gemstone pebbles brought down the River Coquet.

To find other sites of special significance, we have to consider the character of the glacial debris called boulder clay. The gemstones are not evenly distributed throughout the boulder clay, but occur in some concentration in specific areas of clay. Obviously beaches adjacent to boulder clay containing a greater concentration of gemstones are more likely to offer a reasonable selection of specimens.

Beaches which stand out in this respect are to be found in Robin Hood's Bay, at Cornelian Bay near Scarborough and near Hornsea. It is worth noting that the name Cornelian has in the past been used to describe the orange gemstone we now call carnelian. The beaches around Whitby are also good for gemstones, but obviously the more accessible beaches are easily picked over.

The presence of glacial debris is not only confined to the beaches. Very often the same types of pebbles occur in the agricultural land behind the beaches. Fragments of agate and carnelian have been found in fields near Cornelian Bay and farmland around Robin Hood's Bay has yielded examples of a type of hematite which has gemstone characteristics. The hematite is at home in the Lake District and its presence in Yorkshire is purely due to glacial drift.

Amber

Of all the gem materials I have encountered in the North of England, amber is undoubtedly the rarest. Unlike the other gemstones I have described which may be found with considerable ease, amber is very scarce indeed. I have known collectors who have scoured likely beaches over periods of twenty years or more, who have yet to find their first specimen of amber. However, the fact remains that on the coast of Yorkshire, amber is as plentiful as it is anywhere else in Britain.

Amber is in fact not stone, but resin. It originated from certain types of pine trees which flourished during Oligocene Times around 40 million years ago. It is primarily formed from a variable ratio of carbon, hydrogen and oxygen. Unlike other naturally occurring resins which are plentiful today, amber contains a quite considerable quantity of succinic acid and a little sulphur.

It is a soft material having a hardness of 2—2.5 on Mohs' Hardness Scale. Indeed there is very little about amber that is not variable. In colour it is best known for being honey yellow but it may also be redder, whiter or browner than honey and frequently is. It is superb when transparent, but is more often translucent having an internal cloudiness. In any case beach pebbles of amber usually have a frosty outer skin which disguises any natural transparency the stone may possess inside.

Amber is mined at a number of locations on the coast of the Baltic, particularly in Poland, but it also occurs on a number of Baltic beaches. While the Baltic is widely considered to be the home of amber, it also occurs in other parts of the world including the Phillipines.

Sea amber as it is called was found in reasonable quantities on Britain's east coast during the last century, large pebbles up to 3 and 4 inches in diameter being not unusual. Today specimens appear to be scarcer and much smaller. The coastline of Norfolk and Suffolk was particularly productive of amber in the last century, as was the beach near Bridlington. Certainly the most promising area of coastline in the North of England for amber is that between Flamborough Head and Spurn Point, but it is very hard to come by. It is my personal belief that amber may occasionally be found on the majority of Britain's east coast, probably as far north as Aberdeen.

Identifying amber is not difficult when you hold a piece in your hand due to its characteristic lightness, but spotting the right pebble on a beach is rather more of a problem. The shingle on any of the east coast beaches will always contain a large number of yellow quartz pebbles, which to the eye can closely resemble amber. Naturally the quartz is very hard (7 on Mohs' Scale) and the disappointment of finding the pebble is not amber (2—2.5 on Mohs' Scale) is not long in coming. To increase the chance of finding amber on the beach, it is necessary to take advantage of another physical characteristic of the stone, its density.

Amber has a specific gravity of 1 to 1.1 which means it may be slightly buoyant in water. This characteristic buoyancy means that amber will be carried up the beach and deposited at the highest level reached by the incoming tide. The place to look for amber is therefore amongst the seaweed which often marks the high tide mark. The low specific gravity (density) means it is very light and once you pick a specimen of amber off the beach and compare it with the weight of other similar sized pebbles, its character is finally confirmed. At last a small specimen of one of Britain's rarest gemstones can be added to your collection.

Jet

The beaches of the east coast contain many gemstones, but most of them are little more than small pebbles with no usable qualities. The majority of these gemstones have been imported to the coast by one or more of a number of geological processes. Without exception the gemstones we have considered so far were all created many miles from where they are now found and yet on the east coast we have a gemstone which exists 'in situ' in the rocks in which it was created. And in addition it has also formed the basis of a jewellery industry which once ranged the length and breadth of Britain; this gemstone is jet.

Jet is not a mineral, but a rock, and occurs amongst a group of bituminous shales of the Upper Lias on the Yorkshire coast. Jet is a form of fossilized driftwood which has been diagenetically altered. This process resulted in the collapse of the wood structure making subsequent identification impossible.

This gemstone occurs as seams within the upper reaches of the Jet Rock shales and is not common. Two main forms are known, the first being plate-like seams known as 'Plank Jet' which are rarely more than 2 centimetres thick. The second type of jet is called cored jet and is rod shaped with a taper at each end. Specimens normally exhibit a silica (chalcedonized) core.

Jet was certainly used a long way back in history and ornaments worked during the Bronze Age are known. The excavation of Roman sites has also revealed jet jewellery, chiefly rings. Many early historians including Bede made reference to the Black Amber from the east coast. Excavation at Whitby Abbey also yielded crucifixes and rosary beads made of jet.

There can be little doubt that the working of jet had been carried out on a small scale for many centuries in the Whitby area. It was early in the 19th century when a gentleman by the name of Captain Treulett first began working jet by machine and his knowledge and techniques were passed on to others. By 1832 two jet workshops existed in Whitby, but the popular days of jet still lay ahead.

It was during the early days of the 19th century that mourning for the dead started to become a ritual. Indeed it was the beginning of a ritual which would lead to mourning principles we adopt today. On the death of His Highness the Duke of York in 1827, bracelets and necklaces of a black colour were considered desirable and jet fitted the bill. This was to set a trend which would build the jet industry and provide it with a captive market for 50 years.

Queen Victoria wore a black silk dress with jet jewellery in 1850 while in mourning for the Duke of Clarence. There was no doubt now that jet jewellery was an important aspect of mourning. By 1850 seven workshops were making jet products in Whitby and these included Thomas Andrews who would later become jet ornament maker to Queen Victoria.

The death of Prince Albert in 1861 saw the manufacture of jet jewellery and ornaments hit an all-time peak and by 1870 over 1,500 people were employed in the jet industry, for such it had now become. Workshops were opening in Scarborough and over a hundred dealers and workshops now operated in Whitby.

Over the years the jet workers developed the carving and engraving skill necessary to create the beautiful brooches and pendants which came to personify Whitby Jet, and many began to specialize in one or more aspects of the craft. It would not be unusual for one item of jewellery to be passed around a number of craftsmen for each to add his own individual touch where it was most needed.

Her Majesty Queen Victoria imposed the strictest mourning after the death of Prince Albert and this was a period of dark clothing for the majority of her subjects. However the general public's devotion to jet did not last as long as the Queen's and the jet boom lasted only twenty years. By 1884 only 350 jet workers remained in Whitby. Queen Victoria maintained her strict attitude to mourning until 1887 and her Silver Jubilee. At last she relented and was seen on several occasions wearing small items of silver jewellery. The flood gates were opened and silver became very popular, while jet began to settle back into the obscurity from which it had come. By the year 1921 there were only around 40 jet workers in the Whitby area. The main popularity of jet was finally over although it still enjoys considerable sales appeal with summer visitors to the Whitby area today.

Many reports suggest that jet is now a very scarce commodity, but this may not be strictly true. In the past jet was mined, but only on land which was poor from the farming point of view. Bearing in mind that there is no evidence to suggest that jet is other than uniformly distributed, then the gemstone probably occurs under the good agricultural land in the Cleveland/Whitby area from which it has never been removed. However the jet which may still exist will probably never be extractable while the industry is so run down.

Jet was extracted along the coast between Robin Hood's Bay and Boulby and from shallow workings inland near Roseberry Topping and Bilsdale in the Cleveland Hills. Veins of jet are said to extend under the sea in the Whitby area and the erosion of this material provides most of the 'sea jet' which is washed up on beaches from Saltburn all the way southwards to Bridlington, and Spurn Point. Quite large pieces of jet have been found protruding from the boulder clay cliffs which exist on the coast near Scarborough.

The group of shales which are known as the 'Jet Rock', due to the occurrence of jet amongst them, is capped by a limestone known as the Top Jet Dogger. This rock provides an easily recognisable marker when looking for jet in the cliffs. Above this limestone band, which is only 15 centimetres thick, are a group of Bituminous Shales which occasionally yield examples of soft jet. This material is browner in colour than true jet. It is also softer and more brittle.

Although the jet industry has come more or less to an end, examples of jet articles manufactured during the last century are abundant. Most antique shops have examples for sale and if you visit antique markets, jet jewellery will be found on many jewellery stands. This abundance of antique jet jewellery is irrefutable evidence of the tremendous popularity of Britain's black amber in a now distant and more leisurely age.

4. Gemstones of the Lake District

THE Lake District presents us with some of the oldest rocks in the North of England and for the first time the effects of metamorphism can be seen upon the old and battered rocks. But first we must turn back the geological clock and consider the events which shaped the Lake District and created the gemstones that occur.

Approximately 500 million years ago the area, now known as the North of England, was under water. The whole area, including southern Scotland, was the scene of what is now called the Iapetus Ocean. This was a dying ocean and continents which existed both to the north and south were closing in.

One could liken the approaching northern continent to America and the southern continent to Europe. Obviously the Iapetus Ocean was in effect a former Atlantic Ocean. Sediments were being accumulated on the floor of the ocean, but from time to time volcanoes were to become active as the ocean was slowly squeezed out of existence.

Northern Scotland was at this stage part of the North Atlantic Continent while southern Britain formed part of the European Continent. The closing of the Iapetus Ocean was to bring the two sections of the British Isles together.

The coming together of the two continents caused the rocks of the Northern Continent to be pushed up into a huge mountain chain, while a series of volcanic island arcs formed to the south. Time passed and slowly the two continents came together, squeezing and folding the rocks under the tremendous pressure.

The sediments which were being laid down in the floor of the Iapetus Ocean would subsequently be folded up into southern Scotland and northern England. They were slightly modified by the pressure and are known in the Lake District as Skiddaw Slates and are of Ordovician or possibly in one or two instances, of Cambrian Age.

The volcanoes which formed the volcanic island arc, similar to the islands of Japan today, are preserved in the Lake District as the Borrowdale Volcanic Series. Several volcanoes were active in what is now the Lake District and very large quantities of volcanic debris accumulated on the sea floor. The first phases of the vulcanism were explosive and this resulted in the expulsion of large quantities of volcanic ash which exists today in the tuffs, ashes and volcanic breccias[1] of the Lake District. The explosive phases were followed

1. Breccias are composite rocks consisting of angular fragments of stone cemented by lime for example.

by the extrusion of huge quantities of andesitic lavas which flowed fairly rapidly out over the sea floor to accumulate great thicknesses.

At first the volcanoes were submarine, but the huge quantities of lava and ash being accumulated by the various volcanic vents were soon to result in the volcanoes emerging from the sea as volcanic islands. Indeed so rapidly did the volcanoes emerge from out of the sea that much of the volcanic rock flowed on land where it was subjected to equally rapid erosion.

Towards the end of the volcanic phase, considerable earth movements occurred in this area and subsidence followed. In shallow water the Coniston Limestone Group was laid down. These sediments include limestone and sandstone, and are interbedded with lavas and tuffs.

Earth movements continued into the Silurian Period but mudstones, siltstones and sandstones were accumulated on the sea floor without a break. Towards the end of the Silurian Period came the climatic movements of the Caledonian Orogeny. This was the final closing of the Iapetus Ocean and the completion of the huge mountain chain, known today as the Caledonian Mountains. The mountainous tract of land reached Continental proportions and extended from Northern Ireland to Scandinavia. Northern England was part of the foothills of these great mountains.

Throughout the Devonian Period desert conditions prevailed and the erosion of the mountains continued at a fair pace. The compression of the earth's crust buckled the rocks into hills and troughs and induced the slaty cleavage into the rocks of Skiddaw. At, or around, the same time large amounts of igneous material was intruded into the base of the Lake District area. Today, after repeated uplift and erosion, the intrusions are partly exposed as the granites of Eskdale, Shap and Skiddaw. It was in the Cheviot Hills at this time that the igneous material reached the surface to form the volcanic complex. A further granite intrusion was made in the Weardale area of Durham and now underlies the rocks of the Pennines.

For fifty million years the desert conditions persisted until at the dawn of the Carboniferous Period, subsidence of the land surface was followed by incursions by the sea. Various stable blocks existed and the subsidence was anything but uniform. Most of the Lake District remained above sea level until quite late in the Lower Carboniferous Period. Limestones were being laid down in the Carboniferous Sea, although volcanic activity was taking place in the northern area of the Lake District and this resulted in the formation of the Cockermouth Lavas. These volcanic rocks are olivine basalts and they still reach a depth of 100 metres in places.

During the Upper Carboniferous Period, coarse sandstones were formed under deltaic conditions in the Pennine area and this was followed by the great coal forests. The Lake District appears to have by-passed much of this activity and may have existed above sea level at the time. Today the Carboniferous rocks exist in an arc around the northern margins of the Lake District.

Further earth movements brought the Carboniferous Period to a close. The rocks of northern England were uplifted and folded, resulting in the erosion of the Carboniferous rocks. Desert conditions were to prevail for millions of years and in places where areas of water were cut off from the sea, evaporation took place. This resulted in the formation of first, the Magnesium Limestone and later, deposits of gypsum and anhydrite. Such deposits are now the basis of industry in the Vale of Eden.

The Permian and Triassic periods passed away and the landscape slowly sank beneath the sea. Whether the rocks of the Jurassic and Cretaceous periods were ever deposited in the Lake District area is uncertain for only Liassic rocks still exist, these being found near Carlisle. The chalk may have been deposited and subsequently eroded, but no one can be certain.

For over 150 million years the area remained underwater until the onset of the Alpine earth movement uplifted the sea floor and threw the rocks into a dome. Erosion then proceeded to remove the younger rocks on the top of the pile to reveal the older rocks which form the basis of the Lake District. A new river system was developed and over some 25 million years erosion created the basic landscape we know today.

It was left to the repeated glaciations of the Pleistocene Ice Age to add the final touches to the scenery. The Lake District was a centre for glaciation, and at the same time an obstacle to ice flowing from southern Scotland. Lake District ice was deflected eastwards across Yorkshire to the east coast and at one time or another all but possibly the highest peaks of the Lake District mountains were covered by ice.

Finally around 10,000 years ago the ice retreated. As it melted large lakes were formed until the increasing water level caused the water to overspill and escape southwards towards the sea. Large channels were cut in the landscape as the torrents of water escaped. The bare landscape quickly gained a cloak of greenery and life returned to the Lake District scenery.

Mineralization is quite extensive in the rocks of the Lake District and is generally considered to have taken place during Permian Times when desert conditions existed on the surface. The mineralization is predominantly in the form of veins of lead and zinc sulphides, and some copper minerals; with fluorite, baryte, calcite and quartz. Weathering of the veins has resulted in the formation of secondary minerals.

The mineral veins exist in old faults and fissures in the rocks and are usually created as a late stage in the formation of a granite intrusion. In some instances the mineralizing fluids directly replaced limestone, resulting in the formation of quite large ore bodies. The veins were worked extensively during the 18th and 19th centuries and it is said that some reserves still remain in the ground. Little mining takes place today.

The volcanic rocks have been subjected to hydrothermal activity which has resulted in the deposition of minerals and some gemstones in the gas cavities. Metamorphism has also resulted in the formation of new minerals, but this is not a major factor where Lake District minerals are concerned.

Lake District Slate

The Lake District green slate is now famous throughout most of Britain. Its recent rise to popularity as an ornamental stone has resulted in the development of a thriving industry in Cumbria. Ornaments such as table lamps, clocks, barometers and wall plaques form a fundamental part of the industry, but jewellery is also made in quite considerable quantities.

One interesting aspect of slate working is that it need not be polished, in fact with the larger ornaments a freshly hewn look is quite adequate. Indeed the slate will not accept the high polish that was achieved with the Derbyshire limestones, but is none the less popular for that.

Anyone taking a close look at the green slate may realise that it does not exhibit the same degree of cleavage that one normally accepts in traditional roofing slate. In addition the stone is light coloured, where most slates are dark. In fact the Lake District green slate is not slate in the normally accepted sense, but is of volcanic origin.

This attractive stone is consolidated volcanic ash, otherwise called tuff, which has been hardened off to slate grade and exhibits some degree of cleavage. The rock is part of the Borrowdale Volcanic Series and is quite extensive in occurrence. Slate quarries exist at Elterwater and Honister, to name but two locations.

As an ornamental stone, the green slate does not have a long history. However it has been a source of roofing material for many years. While it exhibits cleavage, this is variable and usually less distinct than in more traditional slate metamorphosed from a sedimentary rock. In consequence the roofing tiles on houses in the Lake District area will often appear to be much thicker than slate from other parts of Britain.

The green slate is slightly harder than most of the limestones which have been worked in Derbyshire and is to some extent more durable. However, it is not capable of accepting the high polish which can be achieved with more traditional gemstones. It is frequently worked with diamond cutting tools, especially for sawing into small usable pieces. Of all the lapidary techniques, turning is not frequently employed with green slate, primarily due to the plain character of much of the stone. A rough appearance is in many ways preferable.

Worked examples are plentiful in the Lake District, stocked by the vast majority of gift shops. Rough pieces may be collected at many horizons within the Borrowdale Volcanic Series, but permission is needed to enter specific quarries. Of all the stones which have been the basis of successful businesses in Britain, the Lake District green slate may not be the most exotic, but few others can compete with its explosive origin and the fact that its creation marked the death of a previous Atlantic Ocean, and the original union between England and Scotland.

Hematite

Hematite occurs in nature in a wide variety of forms, one of which is a gemstone. The Lake District has provided a wealth of hematite for more than a century, but this has not been used for ornamental purposes. Indeed the main commercial application for hematite is in the production of pig iron and subsequently steel, for hematite is, in fact, iron ore.

It is in west Cumbria that the hematite deposits occur, close to the small town of Egremont. Many mines once worked the hematite, but since the British Steel Corporation took over some years ago, the deposits are worked from one mine at Beckermet. The hematite is transported by rail to Workington for smelting into pig iron. This is one of the richest ores in Britain with an average iron content of 48 per cent.

The ore occurs as veins in the Carboniferous Limestone and in some areas has directly replaced the limestone, giving rise to large and tabular shaped ore bodies. Much of the ore is present in an impure massive form which is red in colour and has no decorative qualities whatsoever. However within this lower grade ore are pockets of a beautiful black crystalline form of hematite called specularite and a botryoidal or mamillary form which is called kidney ore. Kidney ore can be worked for decorative purposes, while specimens of the glittering specularite are highly attractive and very popular with collectors.

Unlike the famous Lakeland Slate which has been manufactured into ornaments, the hematite is only used for small items of jewellery. When cut and polished for jewellery purposes, the hematite is black with a metallic sheen which gives it a highly attractive appearance.

This stone does not have a large local appeal such as jet or Blue John enjoy, possibly because it has not the same long history of decorative use in the Lake District. Jewellery manufactured from it can be seen in the shops in the area, but quite a large proportion of hematite jewellery is made in other parts of Britain. However this gemstone is universally popular and the British Steel Corporation have sold quite large quantities of kidney ore for transportation to the world's stone cutting centre at Idar Oberstein in Germany. Specimens of specularite which often contain quartz, dolomite, calcite and baryte, have also been sold for distribution through the gift trade in Britain.

Hematite is a difficult stone to work but being relatively soft, around 5—6 on Mohs' Scale, it can be carved, and jewellery incorporating carved intaglios are very popular. On working it gives off a red sludge which is very messy and has, to a large extent, eliminated it as a material for amateurs to work with.

Unfortunately in Cumbria there is no appreciable reserve of hematite in the ground and the future of the mines for any long period of time is doubtful. Extraction reached a peak during the late 19th century and has continued to fall to the present day, although recent estimates indicate that the output from the Egremont mines still accounts for around 60 per cent of Britain's total hematite production (note — these mines may close during 1981).

Unlike Blue John which is unique to Britain, hematite even in its gemstone forms, is common the world over. As a result of this, much of the hematite jewellery on sale in Britain may not necessarily contain the British stone.

Other Lake District Gemstones

The geological processes which have shaped the Lake District have resulted in the creation of a number of gemstones, but by and large they have no commercial value. As the mineral veins have offered little of real gemstone value, it is left to the volcanic rocks to provide the gemstones which occur.

It is the Borrowdale Volcanic Series which provide the Lake District with most of the minor gemstones. In some areas the lavas have suffered hydrothermal activity which has given rise to the deposition of a variety of minerals in the gas cavities. Quartz and chalcedony are represented, but are not plentiful. Carnelian and agate are found together with the common grey chalcedony and the occasional specimen of amethyst is known.

Probably the best publicized location for these gemstones is in the lavas of Walla Crag and Falcon Crag near Keswick. However, I have yet to see any quantity of worthwhile specimens of the silica gemstones from this or any other location in the Borrowdale Volcanic Series. That these gemstones occur is fact, but they lack the qualities which workable gemstones require; indeed they are gemstones in name only. The dark green gemstone epidote also occurs in interesting crystal specimens on Walla Crag.

Another more exotic gemstone occurs quite commonly in the lavas, where in all honesty it does not belong; the stone is garnet. Garnets are normally a product of metamorphism and are only rarely found in volcanic rocks. They are often present in the lavas of the Borrowdale Volcanic Series, sometimes only as microscopic crystals, but on other occasions they reach the size of a pea. Usually they are almandine garnets which are a dark red or wine colour. Specimens of garnet may be found in Cat Ghyll on Walla Crag and at other locations in the area. Unfortunately once again they have no decorative value.

Garnets also occur at Shap in the Shap Blue Quarry. This quarry has been cut into rocks of the Borrowdale Volcanic Series, but here the volcanic rocks have suffered metamorphism due to the near proximity of the Shap granite. These rocks in no way resemble the lavas they once were. Metamorphism has encouraged the formation of garnets in cavities in the rocks and sometimes specimens can measure up to an inch across. The garnets, which are usually found lining cavities in the rocks, frequently exhibit their complex crystal form, but also occur in a massive form with quartz.

Carrock Fell is well known for providing Britain with a wide variety of minerals over the last few centuries and it is here that two gemstones occur. Neither has any decorative value but both have been found as worthwhile specimens; they are apatite, a pale green stone, and tourmaline. Tourmaline would be green or green and pink in its gemstone form, but here it is usually found as the black tourmaline which is known as schorl.

Finally I must outline the character of some of the gemstone pebbles which occur on the beaches of the west coast. The area of coast in question is that to the west of the Lake District.

The beaches here will occasionally yield pebbles of chalcedony, especially carnelian and agate. These gemstones appear to be of Scottish origin and have probably been brought to the area from the north by glacial action during the Ice Age. Glacial deposits in the form of boulder clay do exist along this coast, but are frequently hidden from view by sand dunes. That the gemstones have been eroded from these deposits seems certain, as no exposure of volcanic rock occurs near the coast here.

The coastal scenery is formed from sandstones and shales between Barrow in Furness and Whitehaven, followed by rocks of the Coal Measures which are replaced by sandstones and shales near Maryport. Tall cliffs of sandstone of Triassic Age form the cliffs at St. Bees Head and it is here that one of the most attractive beaches on this stretch of coast occurs. It is the beach at Fleswick Bay, which has been carved out of the sandstones of the headland. This beach is renowned for its beautifully shaped pebbles which have been well smoothed and rounded by the tide in this small bay. The pebbles on the beach are chiefly of Lake District origin but include agate, carnelian and a dark red jasper. The beach also yields a yellow stone which is banded and resembles agate, although it appears to be rather more closely related to chert. Fleswick Bay can be reached by walking either north over the cliffs from the village of St. Bees or southwards from St. Bees lighthouse.

With the exception of Fleswick Bay, the gemstone pebbles are more or less evenly distributed along the coast. Indeed any reasonable concentration of pebbles on this stretch of coast is likely to yield examples of the gemstones. However, make no mistake, the gemstone pebbles here are nowhere as common as they are on the east coast.

KEY TO GEOLOGICAL MAP OF LAKE DISTRICT

SEDIMENTARY ROCKS

Rocks of Jurassic Age

Rocks of Triassic Age

Rocks of Permian Age

Rocks of Carboniferous Age

Coal Measures

Millstone Grit Series

Carboniferous Limestone Series

Rocks of Silurian Age

Rocks of Ordovician and Cambrian Ages

IGNEOUS ROCKS

Volcanic
Cockermouth Lavas of Carboniferous Age
Borrowdale Volcanic Series of Ordovician Age

Intrusive

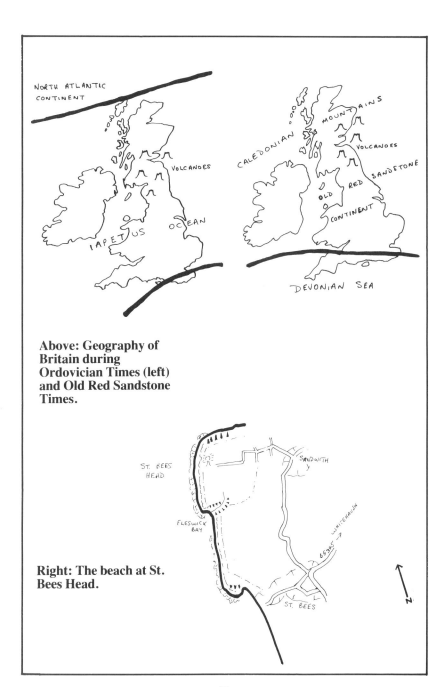

NORTH ATLANTIC
CONTINENT

VOLCANOES

IAPETUS OCEAN

CALEDONIAN MOUNTAINS

VOLCANOES

OLD RED SANDSTONE
CONTINENT

DEVONIAN SEA

Above: Geography of Britain during Ordovician Times (left) and Old Red Sandstone Times.

ST. BEES HEAD

SANDWITH

FLESWICK BAY

WHITEHAVEN

A595

N

ST. BEES

Right: The beach at St. Bees Head.

Agate bearing volcanic rocks are exposed in the River Coquet near Windyhaugh.

Agate from the northern Cheviots near Wooler.

Above — Top: The beach at Amble near the mouth of the River Coquet. Bottom: The beach at Cornelian Bay near Scarborough.

Opposite: Jewellery and ornaments carved out of Whitby Jet, from the collection of Mrs. J. Moralee.   (Photos: G. Wolfendale)

45

Above — Top: Hematite from the Beckermet Mine, Cumbria. Bottom: Dice manufactured from Lakeland Slate by Ian and Rhona Matthews of Kirkby Stephen.

Opposite — Top: A bowl made from Derbyshire alabaster. Bottom left: Blue John. Bottom right: An inlaid Black Marble plaque, from the collection of Mrs. J. Moralee. (Photo: G. Wolfendale)

KEY TO THE GEOLOGICAL MAP OF THE PENNINES

SEDIMENTARY ROCKS

IGNEOUS ROCKS

Rocks of Carboniferous Age
Coal Measures

Intrusive

Millstone Grit Series

Volcanic

Carboniferous Limestone Series

Rocks other than those of
Carboniferous Age

5.   Gemstones of the Pennines

THE Pennine Hills straddle Northern England and have long been known as Britain's backbone. The hills rise out of the plain of midland England and stretch out to the north and north-west almost all the way to the Scottish Border. For the most part the Pennines are not particularly high, but despite this they have proved a very effective barrier over the centuries. Even today a relatively small accumulation of snow can bring traffic travelling across the Pennines to a complete standstill.

In Derbyshire the Pennines rise to a height of around 2,000 feet, but acquire greater stature further north in Yorkshire where at Whernside they reach 2,200 feet and at Cross Fell in Cumbria they reach around 2,500 feet. The southern Pennines are less spectacular though more friendly than the more northerly hills, but barren moorlands are an inherent feature of the Pennine landscape.

Excluding the coast, the Pennines form the main basis for a wide range of pleasure and leisure activities and every year thousands of people try to lose themselves amongst their beautiful scenery. That the beautiful hills and dales should become a tourist centre is understandable when one considers the many centres of population which stand in their shadow. In numerous parts of Britain tourism would be a problem but, with one or two exceptions, the Pennines seem to soak up people and even on the busiest day a determined person can escape from the madding crowd.

The beauty of the Pennines was largely determined by the geology of the rocks which form them and to find the origins of the Pennine Hills, we will have to return to a period over 300 million years. Although not a long time by geological standards, the last 300 million years have seen many primary changes in the British landscape.

Four hundred million years ago northern Britain was part of a large mountain chain. Northern England formed part of the foothills of this mountain range. Around this time, in what are now the Cheviot Hills, a volcano was active, but this was soon to dwindle away and as the years passed, the foothills were eroded almost down to sea level.

Approximately 320 million years ago, the landscape which made up this northern part of England began to subside and the sea came to cover large areas of countryside. Subsidence was not uniform over the entire area and one or two islands were left protruding above the water, which in any case was only shallow.

The climate in this part of the world was warm and dry, and little erosion was taking place on the northern mountains. The rivers flowing from the north were not fast flowing and carried little in the way of eroded debris into the shallow sea. The absence of eroded particles meant that the seas were clear and sparkling, and life of many types was able to proceed uninterrupted.

Life of one form or another had already existed on the earth for 3,000 million years and now it was becoming quite diverse. Many of the creatures had the ability to secrete lime out of sea water to form hard shells and skeletons. When the creatures died, their hard remains fell to the sea floor to add to a growing mass of lime rich sediment, which was limestone in the making.

The greatest limestone builders were the corals which thrived in huge colonies in this ancient sea. They were to build huge epitaphs which would one day dominate the Pennine scene. Conditions suitable for the formation of limestone were to continue for over 20 million years, but there were minor distractions.

In fact the distractions took the form of a number of small volcanoes which were active in what is now Derbyshire. The volcanoes may have taken the form of volcanic islands, or may have been simply fissures in the earth's crust which allowed volcanic rock to well up on to the sea floor. There were, however, large quantities of volcanic ash thrown out of the vents and these were also accumulated on the sea floor to be interbedded with the limestones.

Although several volcanic vents were active over a period of 20 million years, it is doubtful if any of the vents were active simultaneously. It is known, however, that a number of igneous intrusions were made around this time. These took the form of sills and dykes and were not totally restricted in occurrence to Derbyshire.

The volcanoes passed away and the seas returned to their former conditions. Lime sediment continued to be laid down on the sea floor and great depths were accumulated. The stable island-like blocks which had resisted the early subsidence of the sea floor finally succumbed and conditions seemed set for a long period of relative stability.

But stability there was not to be, and it was not long before uplift of the northern mountains combined with the onset of a wetter monsoon-like climate had brought the life span of the limestone sea to a close. The modification of the environment resulted in the development of faster flowing rivers in the north. Erosion proceeded at a rapid pace and the rivers were now carrying large quantities of debris towards the sea.

Slowly at first, but then more rapidly, the finer debris was washed southwards where it finally settled to the bottom, subsequently to form shale. Clear conditions returned for a time, but as the sea gradually became cloudy, the creatures which had thrived in the sparkling clear waters began to leave the area. The formation of limestone, which surprisingly is an important aspect when considering gemstones of northern England, was suspended. Limestones would be formed intermittently over a long period of time, but these would only form minor parts of the succession.

As the years passed the Carboniferous Sea became largely infilled with debris. At first the debris was fine, but part of the Pennine area was soon to come under the influence of a river delta and the finer particles were periodically replaced by coarse sands which ultimately produced the sandstones known as Millstone Grit.

The accumulation of the river debris resulted in the formation of sand and mud banks which emerged above water level. Life, which now included many land plants, became established on the mud banks; and before many millions of years had passed, dense forests towered out of the swamp land. On their death the trees fell into the swamp and were ultimately transformed into coal. The trees and swamps of the coal forest were to survive for many millions of years before the landscape began to change once again.

This time the Pennine area was to suffer uplift. A large mountain chain was being formed away to the south-east and Britain was on the fringe of this uplift. In the shadow of these Amorcian Mountains, desert conditions were to come to this area. The southern part of Britain was thrown into a series of gentle folds and erosion began to remove the upper layers of the exposed rocks.

Being soft, the rocks of the Coal Measures were quickly removed by erosion and then areas of Millstone Grit suffered the same fate. With the limestone partially exposed, the whole area was subjected to subsidence and debris eroded from the nearby mountains was piled up on top.

While desert conditions existed on the surface, the rocks of the Pennines now existed far below the ground under an ever increasing weight of debris. And underground they would remain for almost 200 million years. On the surface the desert conditions gave way to sea, but land would return ultimately. The dinosaurs prowled the land, sea and air; but would leave not a mark on the Pennine landscape which was still preserved far below the earth's surface.

Geography of Britain during the Lower Carboniferous (Carboniferous Limestone Times).

Eventually the process went into reverse and the rocks of England were once again thrown into a series of gentle folds. The land emerged above sea level and erosion commenced. As the millions of years passed, the young rocks which had been deposited above the long established limestones, sandstones, and coal of the Pennines were eroded away, leaving a landscape very similar to the one we enjoy today.

Further modifications were made by glaciers during the Pleistocene Ice Age, but there is some doubt as to whether or not the ice actually overcame the highest areas of the Pennines. The hills probably acted as a centre for glaciation, but glacial deposits such as may have existed on the Pennines have largely been removed by subsequent erosion. And so the Pennines became the hills they are today, although all the vegetation covering the hills is only the result of the last 10,000 years, since the end of the last glaciation.

Today the limestones formed in the Carboniferous Sea are exposed in Derbyshire, Yorkshire and Durham where they form the most attractive dales scenery. The sandstones known as Millstone Grit are the basis of the barren moorland scenery which is also a prominent feature of the Pennines. The rocks of the Coal Measures which include sandstones, siltstones and mudstones as well as coal are usually only found on the fringes of the Pennines and are not a prominent feature of the Pennine scene.

Mineralization of the rocks of the Pennines has taken two main forms and each has produced gemstones on a small scale. The primary mineralization is of the limestone and in fact took place a long time following the creation of the limestone itself.

It was during the time the rocks of the Pennines were deep underground that the mineralization took place. This was around 200 million years ago. Subsequent tests which have been carried out to determine precisely the age of the mineral veins within the limestone, have indicated that the mineralization took place over a period of time spanning many millions of years.

The mineralization took the form of sulphide veins containing ores of lead and zinc, but include some copper and other minerals such as fluorite, baryte, quartz and calcite. This type of mineralization is often associated with a granite type intrusion, but as yet no direct correlation exists between Derbyshire's mineral veins and a so far undetected granite mass below ground. Further north a large granite mass has been found beneath Weardale, but this has been proved to be of much greater age even than the limestone. We are left, therefore, with the further conclusion that there is yet another granite intrusion underlying the ancient one, deep below the northern Pennines.

It has also been suggested that the mineralization in Derbyshire is due, not to granite type intrusion, but to minor faulting deep within the earth's crust at the time the rocks were buried. The main difference which exists between the mineralization in the northern and southern Pennines is the presence of quartz within the veins. In Derbyshire quartz is absent from the veins while in Durham and Northumberland, the mineral is abundant.

The mineral veins are mainly confined to the limestone and are only rarely found in the sandstones and shales above. This is because limestone is readily soluble in the mineralizing fluids while shale will often be insoluble and will act as a cap rock preventing their upward movement.

Whatever their precise origin may be, the mineral veins of the Pennines have provided the basis for man's existence in this part of Britain for over 2,000 years. They were most heavily exploited during the 18th and 19th centuries when the Industrial Revolution was in full swing. The interest then was in lead ore, but today the accent has changed and it is fluorite and baryte which are most sought after in the Pennines.

The second type of mineralization which has overtaken the rocks of the Peak District is restricted to the volcanic rocks. Hydrothermal activity similar to that which took place in the volcanic rocks of the Cheviot Hills was to have considerable influence upon the character of Derbyshire's igneous rocks.

Unlike the Cheviot Hills, where silica was the main material deposited in the cracks and vesicals of the volcanic rocks, in Derbyshire calcite was one of the principal minerals. This was probably due to the quite considerable quantity of limestone deposits in the surrounding area. Silica was also deposited hydrothermally, but is usually most prominent close to the centre of the volcanic assemblage; in other words away from the limestone margins.

The deposition of silica did mean that gemstones could be formed and to some extent they were, but not in any great quantity. Indeed the silica is usually present as quartz, in a massive crystalline form or as small colourless crystals. Crypto-crystalline silica or chalcedony is much scarcer than the coarsely crystalline variety and is restricted in occurrence to only a few of the igneous rock exposures in the southern Pennines.

The hydrothermal activity did have the effect of modifying the volcanic rocks quite considerably. The modification was largely to the detriment of the rocks which today frequently exhibit extensive decomposition. The intrusive igneous rocks, which chiefly take the form of dolerite, may also show decomposition and weathering, but are not as extensively mineralized. In fact it is these rocks which have been used commercially for road building purposes rather than their volcanic relatives.

Hydrothermal minerals in the igneous rocks of the southern Pennines have no commercial application, although a number of attempts were made more than a century ago. The lavas are known locally as Toadstone and were disliked by the local lead miners because the lead veins in the limestone came to an abrupt halt where they met the lavas and rarely continued on the other side. Like the shales and sandstones of the Millstone Grit series, the volcanic rocks acted as a cap rock preventing the upward passage of the mineralizing fluids.

Blue John

The mineralization of the Carboniferous Limestone, which is exposed in the Pennines, was very extensive and a number of common minerals were formed. One of these common minerals is called fluorite (it used to be called fluorspar) and is composed of calcium and fluorine with the chemical formula CaF_2. For many centuries fluorite had no commercial value, but this has changed and the mineral is much sought after for use in the steel industry. Now it is used as a flux in steel smelting, but it is also used in the manufacture of hydrofluoric acid. The Pennines now stand as one of the world's largest producers of this mineral.

Fluorite is a very common mineral and occurs usually in massive form, or may exhibit cubic crystals. It would be colourless if pure, but is quite commonly found in a wide variety of colours varying from green and yellow to pink and purple. Green fluorite is rare, especially as crystals, but the other colours are more or less widespread even as crystal specimens. There is, however, one type of fluorite which has rather different characteristics. It is a banded form, the bands being purple and colourless, with yellow in varying amounts. This banded type of fluorite is virtually unique to one part of the world. It comes from near the village of Castleton in Derbyshire and is called Blue John.

Blue John fluorite is a series of pipe veins in the limestone of Treak Cliff, a hill near Castleton. As far as is known these veins are contemporaries of the other mineral veins which occur in the Derbyshire area, but the precise age is not certain due to the inherent variation in the age of the veins which occur locally. The Blue John veins do not contain any appreciable content of other minerals, a fact which sets them apart from a number of more conventional sulphide veins which occur in the same hill, and have yielded quite a variety of minerals.

The origin of Blue John has given mineralogists cause for considerable argument over the last century on account of its banded character. There are, however, certain other peculiar features in the geology of the Castleton area. One of these is the presence of the hydrocarbon minerals which occur, and can be seen in situ, in the small quarry at Windy Knoll. These minerals were probably derived from organic remains within the limestone, and were modified to their existing form by the hot mineralizing fluids which created the mineral veins. The hydrocarbon minerals are slightly radioactive.

Although conflicting reports exist, it is generally considered that the blue and white banded character of Blue John is due to the imprisonment of hydrocarbon compounds within the fluorite at the

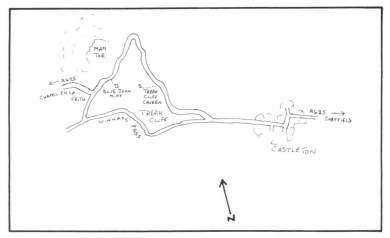

Treak Cliff at Castleton, the home of Blue John.

time of its formation. However, the beautiful coloured structure of Blue John may be due to lattice defects within the atomic structure of the stone created by the effects of radioactivity. Certain analyses have indicated that there is little difference in composition between the colourless and blue areas of the stone, which tends to confirm the radiation theory. At the same time other physical characteristics of the stone on heating tend to contradict this belief. Of course it may be that both theories have contributed to the formation of Blue John.

Blue John is a very special stone for it is the only true gemstone in the Pennines which has been worked commercially for ornamental purposes. And yet in so many ways the stone is unsuitable for the purpose. It is a soft stone, being equivalent to 4 on Mohs' Scale of Hardness, and it is coarsely crystalline which also means it is predictably brittle. Cutting the stone and setting it into jewellery, or manufacturing ornaments are tasks which are fraught with difficulty. For ease of working, and in an attempt at increasing the durability of the stone, it is standard practice to impregnate Blue John in natural resin. However now that more modern techniques, such as capping the Blue John with a quartz cap can be used, this may help to make the jewellery a better purchase. Despite these disadvantages, Blue John is extremely popular and its jewellery and ornaments are much prized.

There is little or no evidence to suggest that Blue John was worked before the late 17th century. Certainly it is doubtful if the Romans knew of its existence at the time of their occupation of the area. Vases made from a material similar to Blue John were found in the ruins of Pompeii. However, bearing in mind that these are the only possible examples of Blue John which date prior to the 17th

55

century, it is hardly surprising that mineralogists believe the Roman examples are made from a stone which was being imported into Rome from Persia at the time.

That the Romans exploited the mineral veins of the Pennines is a certainty, but subsequent working during the last three hundred years has virtually destroyed any evidence of Roman activity that may have existed. It is possible, therefore, that the Romans did not work the lead ore close to Treak Cliff where the discovery of Blue John would have been likely. The Danes extracted lead ore from the Odin Mine which is situated very close to where the Blue John veins occur, but it seems they never stumbled across it. This mine continued working into the 19th century and its workings had extended under a large area of countryside, but by now the Blue John veins had been discovered.

The lead mining laws, many of which are still in force today, were very powerful indeed. They allowed the lead miner the right of access to any property to search for lead ore, regardless of the land owner's wishes. It was apparently lead miners exploring Treak Cliff near Castleton for lead ore who eventually found Blue John and made the exploitation of the stone possible.

At first the extraction of Blue John went ahead slowly, but as methods of utilizing it were developed, it became more popular and before long it was being worked indiscriminately.

Large ornaments became the order of the day, but a number of craftsmen including Robert Adam were to use the stone for decorative inlay work. Indeed this well known craftsman used Blue John for inlay in his famous fireplace at Kedleston Hall in Derbyshire in the 18th century. As the years passed, the craftsmanship was to develop until there existed a thriving industry working Blue John and other local stones.

Large amounts of Blue John were shipped to France in the early days, for here it was to be used in the production of decorative ormolu work. The name Blue John may well have originated at this time. The name is believed to have come from the French Bleu-jaune which means blue and yellow, the principal colours in Blue John fluorite. It is also possible that the name was coined to distinguish the gemstone from another mineral which at the time was called Black Jack. As Black Jack was also known as Zinc Blende the need to differentiate between it and Blue John seems doubtful. However, one would have expected the name to have originated here prior to the stone being exported, hence even the 'French connection' must be in some doubt.

As the years passed an increasing number of people came to appreciate the beauty of Blue John and more famous craftsmen sought to turn the stone to advantage. Matthew Boulton was keen to obtain a large quantity of the stone and in 1768 he endeavoured to obtain a monopoly of the production from all the Blue John mines at Castleton. It is recorded that he obtained only 14 tons of the gemstone at a price of £5 15s. 6d. per ton. At this time the total output from the mine was around 20 tons per year.

A large number of vases and smaller ornaments were made from the stone during the early days and numerous examples have survived into the 20th century. Many, if not most, of Britain's stately homes have an example or two in their collections, and here they can still be seen and admired today. However, the production of such large items in Blue John was nearing an end, and the stone would never be used in such large quantities again.

As the 18th century came to a close, three mines were working Blue John and these were the Treak Cliff, the Old Tor Mine and the Blue John Mine, although it is possible that other less important surface workings existed. By now it was becoming obvious that Blue John was not as plentiful as had at first been assumed. Consequently, extraction of the stone was greatly reduced to around 3 tons per year. Obviously, large items could not so readily be made and so small ornaments and jewellery began to come to the fore. Today, despite a thriving jewellery trade, it is calculated that the total Blue John extracted per year probably varies between ½ and 1 ton.

Blue John continued to be used for inlay work throughout the 19th century, although dependence upon it became much reduced, the craftsmen giving their attention in part to other stones. Indeed other local Derbyshire stones were to come more to the fore and local craftsmen would earn high honours for their workmanship. And so Blue John, while still used as a form of adornment for large ornaments, was now relegated to a position of secondary importance as far as most craftsmen were concerned.

Of course it does not matter how scarce or valuable a material may be, at times of national crisis everything has to be utilized to help the cause. During the First World War the government, determined that every available aspect of Britain's mineral wealth should be utilized to the common good, decided to mine Blue John for use in the steel industry and this they did. For most of the war and for several years afterwards the stone was worked for this purpose, mining only coming to an end during the 1920s. There can be little doubt that considerable inroads were made into the reserves of Blue John during this period, and this has resulted in the stone being a good deal scarcer than it need have been.

One might with some justification ask how scarce the stone is today. Is Blue John in danger of running out? These questions are difficult to answer, the full facts not being available. We know that extraction of the stone is limited today, but regardless of scarcity, controlled extraction is good sense if the industry is to survive over long periods of time. Another factor one may wish to bear in mind is the added impetus sales may enjoy when the commodity has a rarity factor. Blue John undoubtedly has this scarcity value, probably deservedly, but one cannot overlook the possibility that unworked reserves may exist which have not been discovered or fully appreciated.

The government's mining activities during the First World War led to the discovery of the stalactite and stalagmite filled caverns which now form an attractive feature of the Treak Cliff Cavern. This is one of two Blue John mines now open to the public. The Treak Cliff Cavern and the Blue John Mine both offer opportunities for the public to see Blue John in situ in the limestone and this raises another point regarding the scarcity of the stone.

It must be considered that it is better for members of the public to pay to see the stone in situ, rather than pay to take it away in the form of jewellery. Generations of people may enjoy seeing the stone in the mines, while in the long term only a relative few can share the privilege of taking it away. Blue John may therefore in some cases be worth more in the ground than it is out of it.

Fourteen different coloured varieties of Blue John have been established within Treak Cliff, but only very few are exploited today. Each of the different types has been classified in relation to its colour and pattern. It is, however, only the common purple-blue banded varieties which are utilized for jewellery purposes. Such names as the Bully Beef Vein, the Winnats One Vein and the Old Tor Vein are used to describe the different varieties. Antiques manufactured from the rarer veins will obviously enjoy considerably greater value than items made from the more common varieties, but unfortunately the brittle nature of the stone and the elaborate settings needed to support it can make today's jewellery a costly item. Small numbers of bowls and polished eggs are made today and are probably worth considering as small, but profitable investments as the stone's scarcity grows.

Blue John can be seen to advantage in the Treak Cliff Cavern where a very beautiful pillar of the stone has been left in the centre of part of the workings. Blue John is again visible in the Blue John Cavern, but these are not the only parts of the hill where the stone occurs. The third of the mines, the Old Tor Mine, is situated high on the hill overlooking the Winnats Pass. It has been derelict for many years and is largely worked out. On the hill above, Blue John has been found at a number of places sometimes in situ, but often as loose debris. These may be the remnants of Blue John from veins of limestone which were eroded during the million years of the Pleistocene Ice Age.

Collecting Blue John is strongly discouraged in the area and is effectively illegal whether on private land or National Trust property. However there is no reason why one should not climb the Winnats Pass to the top of the Old Tor Mine and examine the Blue John where it is exposed in the limestone cliff. On the way you may pass hollows on the surface of the hill which mark the places from which Blue John has been removed, and undoubtedly at some stage you will see small pieces glistening amongst the soil or scree. It takes little imagination to see the beauty of Blue John, but what a shame our ancestors allowed their enthusiasm to run away with them and leave us with the scarce stone that we know today.

Limestone or Marble

Limestone forms an important part of the scenery of the Pennines. Indeed many would argue that the limestone with its scarps and dales is the key to the real beauty of the hills. Limestone is usually grey in colour and it may contain few, or many, recognisable fossils. This is not surprising as it was made from an accumulation of lime sediment on the floor of the ancient Carboniferous Sea. As a grey, or even white rock, it does much to brighten up the countryside but a hand specimen, unless it exhibits clearly recognisable fossils, will do little to fire the imagination or arouse interest. And yet limestones were once the basis for a highly successful industry which thrived in the Pennines.

This industry, which was based upon the working of the limestones, really began in the Derbyshire Dales, but was to spread on a small scale to the northern Pennines. The earliest example of a worked limestone in the Pennines was found in a tumulus on Fin Cop, to the north of the village of Ashford in the Water. This was a dressed slab of black limestone which dated back to prehistoric times. Indeed it was to be the same black limestone which would form the mainstay of the 19th century marble industry.

The name marble was, and in some circles still is used to describe a limestone which has been polished and used for decorative purposes. Consequently the black limestone found near Ashford in the Water became known to craftsmen as the Ashford Black Marble. A brown striped limestone from Nettler Dale also in Derbyshire, became known as Rosewood Marble. In geological circles the name marble is given to a limestone which has been recrystallized by metamorphism and as such cannot possibly apply to these Pennine limestones. Here is an instance where the same name means different things to different people and confusion frequently follows. Today the geological definition holds sway, but the use of the old names can still cause problems.

That the interest in working limestones should come to the fore in Derbyshire was perhaps inevitable, bearing in mind the tradition for working stone which existed in the area. Blue John, the famous gemstone, was becoming scarce by 1800 and many craftsmen had to turn their attention to other, and more readily available stones. During the early years of the 19th century, the Derbyshire limestones were being increasingly used for decorative purposes.

The Derbyshire craftsmen were fortunate that in the area quite a number of workable limestones occurred. The black limestone from Ashford, which was first mined around the late 17th century, was probably the most popular of the stones, but the harder Rosewood Marble from Nettler Dale was also much used. Unlike the black colouration in the Ashford Marble, which was due to the presence of carbonaceous matter in the limestone, the beautiful rosewood colouration was simply due to the presence of iron oxide. The Bird's Eye Marble from Wetton and the Mottled Grey Marble from Monyash were both highly fossiliferous, the former containing the remains of primitive sea lilies called crinoids, the latter exhibiting small corals.

Being uniformly black in colour and available in fairly large slabs, the Ashford Black Marble provided an ideal base for inlay work using colourful gemstones, but in fact true inlay work was not to be developed for some time to come. Until around 1810 the Derbyshire craftsmen produced nothing more elaborate than veneered mosaic work surfaces. Patchwork or scrap surfaced tables were on sale at this time, the table top consisting of a flat slab of limestone which was covered with irregular shaped slices of coloured marbles and fluorite, the surface being ground and polished.

The year 1810 seems to be significant for it was around this date that the marble craftsmen began cutting the gemstones into predetermined geometric shapes. The gemstone slabs were then cemented in a simple pattern before grinding and polishing. This marked a significant advancement in the craftsmen's skill and provided a more appealing product.

Large and weighty items of furniture were the order of the day during the early 19th century and it became fashionable to place a slab of marble on the top of sideboards, shelves and tables. This practice was soon to lose popularity but tables, chests, chess boards and cupboard panels, together with smaller items such as boxes and paperweights were to remain popular for many years to come.

By the late 1830s the mosaic work was beginning to be replaced by true inlay work in the Florentine 'pietra dura' style. The first craftsman to adopt this type of work was reputedly John Adam of Matlock and as we have already seen with Blue John, his craftsmanship was second to none. The basic principle of this true inlay work was cut to shape out of a slab of marble and infill it very precisely with a slab of gemstone, fluorite or more colourful marble. The work was carried out to a predetermined design and resulted in the creation of an interesting and colourful pattern in the marble slab.

The patterns became beautifully exotic, and included butterflies, birds, flowers and foliage. Colours were exact and the most realistic inlays were created.

Not surprisingly, the Duke of Devonshire had a very large collection of the real Florentine 'pietra dura' at Chatsworth, and he made this available to the local craftsmen to copy. As the years passed so the Derbyshire marble workers became adept at fashioning the most elegant and beautiful items out of their rather unusual raw material.

The Derbyshire limestones had a number of advantages over the Italian varieties and over the years the local craftsmen exploited them wherever possible. In the first place the Derbyshire limestones were soft and could be more easily fashioned than their Continental relatives. They could also be easily stained to give the maximum variety of colours for inlay purposes. For a time the items made in the southern Pennines were able to be sold at prices below that of their main foreign competitors.

Derbyshire's first marble mill had been opened by Henry Watson in 1748 at Ashford, but now mills were opening in all the major towns including Bakewell, Buxton, Castleton, Derby and Matlock. The black limestone from Ashford became extremely popular and in 1832 a new mine was opened in the Rookery Plantation near Ashford, so that the stone could be mined below the surface. This was followed in 1847 by the opening of a quarry near Green Cowden.

Another unique red limestone was found in a lead mine in Alport around 1830 and although very little of it was used, a number of examples do exist, the most striking being the carved pillars in Edensor Church. Much of this stone was stored at Chatsworth; it was called the Duke's Red Marble.

Many different types of ornaments and larger items were now being made. These included snuff and jewellery boxes, paper-weights, chests, bookcases, tables and fireplaces. By 1850 over fifty master craftsmen were producing inlay and mosaic work, and John Adam of Matlock was commissioned by Queen Victoria to make a table of the round pedestal variety. The pillar was fluted and the top was inlaid with foliage, flowers and a number of very beautiful butterflies. Truly the marble industry had reached its zenith.

In 1851 the Derbyshire craftsmen received the highest of honours for their workmanship at the Great Exhibition in Crystal Palace. Sweeping all competition before them, this was the craftsmen's finest hour because progress, moving inexorably onwards, had a final overpowering competitor waiting in the wings.

As in all industries there was a place for automation in the craftsmen's workshops. Turbines were used late in the 19th century at the Ashford Mill and steam powered saws were used to cut the marble into thin panels. Whichever marble was being used, it was essential to select panels which were free from white blemishes or veins of calcite which were common in the stones.

Tables were made in a variety of shapes including octagonal, hexagonal and circular, but the latter was much more popular. The shape of the table was cut out of the marble slab using a mallet and pointed chisel. This shape was bonded to an iron lathe chuck and turned to the desired shape using a pointed lathe tool of high quality tempered steel.

The rough shaped table was then smoothed with a piece of coarse natural sandstone, the surface being water cooled. This operation removed the marks left by the lathe tool, and the marks left by the coarse sandstone were removed by repeating the operation using a finer sandstone. The final operation prior to polishing was to smooth the surface with flour emery before polishing with tin oxide, a white powder.

Large quantities of Pennine marbles were exported to the Continent to be worked and here they were inlaid in the Italian style with semi-precious stones such as agate, chalcedony, carnelian and jasper. Eventually the use of these stones achieved popularity in England, but as specimens of usable value could not be found locally, supplies were imported. Even malachite from Russia was imported for this purpose.

The latter days of the 19th century saw the marble industry pass away, never to return. The final threat came when a new type of ornamental table was put on to the market by G. E. Magnus of Pimlico. These tables were made from slate which was given an artificial surface by being repeatedly baked with japanned ornamentation. In effect this created a synthetic copy of the marble tables.

Slate was abundant compared with the limestones and it was less brittle. Consequently a more durable product was on offer and it was lighter and cheaper. In the face of such competition the marble trade was doomed.

The slate imitation marble tables first came on to the market in the early 1850s, and took many years before they became popular, but when they did, they swept all before them. By 1895 only one marble craftsman remained in business in north Derbyshire, and the marble mill at Ashford in the Water where it all began, closed in 1905.

The remains of the marble industry are not plentiful. The old marble mill at Ashford has gone along with the rest, and only the stone remains. The old mines and quarries are still in existence and the stones that they once produced in such great quantities may be picked up by anyone with sufficient interest. This is particularly true of the Rosewood Marble and the Bird's Eye Marble. The cream Hopton Wood limestone is still worked commercially, but not for the same purposes.

In the Yorkshire Dales the Dent Marble was worked similarly to those in Derbyshire and was essentially a black limestone. In Durham the famous Frosterly Marble was much used. This limestone is composed of white corals set in a dark black matrix, which sets the corals off to considerable advantage. This stone is still quarried at Frosterly today. The same coral limestone is also found on the east coast of Scotland near Dunbar.

All these limestones date back in time to the Carboniferous Sea; a time over 300 million years ago when stability of a sort existed in the Pennine area. The marble industry, based on the ancient limestones, knew stability for a period of fifty years before becoming obsolete in the face of new technology.

Today, examples of the marble industry can be seen in many museums and stately homes in Derbyshire and Yorkshire. Unfortunately the vases and tables did not wear well and only a small proportion of the items made have survived the years. However, the beauty and elegance of the ornamental ware which can still be seen today is a fitting tribute to a marble industry which thrived more than a hundred years ago.

Alabaster

On the southern fringe of the Pennines, the Carboniferous rocks are overlain by younger sedimentary rocks which were formed during the Triassic Period around 220 million years ago. These rocks are primarily limestones and pebble beds, but they include substantial deposits of gypsum which is mainly present as alabaster.

Alabaster is a soft stone which is easily worked into ornaments such as table lamps, ash trays and small vases. The alabaster worked at Chellaston for many years is chiefly white in colour, but in Staffordshire brown and orange colourations in alabaster are common. The alabaster was formed by the repeated evaporation of water, rich in the appropriate minerals. The salt deposits of Cheshire were formed in the same way under extremely arid conditions.

The earliest known working of alabaster in this area dates back to the 14th century, the stone being used mainly for church decoration. Altar pieces were being made and transported to France, Spain and Italy early in the 15th century. It was the Reformation which finally brought this trade to an end.

This soft stone has continued to be worked on a small scale over the last 200 years and is still popular today. However, being soft, the stone is very delicate and has never been useful in an everyday environment, as were the limestones. The stone is readily soluble in water and as many housewives have found, the polished surface of a vase is quickly lost if water is placed in it. Items manufactured today are frequently lacquered to prevent this taking place. Foreign alabaster is frequently seen in shops and has often been dyed into a range of lurid and unnatural colours, which are extremely popular.

Other Gemstones

The Pennines do not contain any significant quantity of gemstones of the more common types. The mineralization of the Pennine limestone resulted in the formation of many minerals which are useful to man, but very few stones have any gemstone qualities.

Galena, lead ore, with its beautiful metallic lustre has been used for inlay work, but only in small amounts, and the same is true of some types of baryte. Oakstone, which is a unique form of baryte, resembles the colour and appearance of wood. This stone has also been used for decorative purposes in inlay work, but has seldom been used for decorative items in its own right. Alongside Blue John, Oakstone is now being worked on a small scale at a gemstone exhibition in Matlock Bath.

The volcanic rocks of the Peak District contain examples of a number of silica gemstones, but these are rarely in a workable form. The old quarry called Calton Hill has yielded amethyst, rock crystal, smoky quartz, jasper and an occasional agate, but most of the quarry has now been reclaimed by landscaping. Olivine, spinel and pyroxene occur together as xenoliths[1] in the Calton Hill lavas and being high temperature minerals, were transported to their present position in a solid state by the molten lavas. They are not hydrothermal minerals, but olivine and spinel are gemstones when they achieve their full beauty, as they do in other lands. In Derbyshire they are present only as small green crystals with little appeal.

At Waterswallow Quarry near Buxton, amethyst, rock crystal, smoky quartz, agate and chalcedony occur, but not in any quantity or quality. The agates are rarely bigger than 3 centimetres in diameter. Agates of similar proportions occur in Millersdale, in the volcanic rocks, and some serpentine occurs near Knock Hill; all of which is very promising, but in reality very disappointing.

Chert is a feature of the limestone, both in Derbyshire and the Yorkshire Dales. It occurs as bands within the Limestone at a number of horizons, and probably originated from silica bearing organisms which thrived in the Carboniferous Sea and added their remains to ooze on the sea floor. Some fossils are preserved in the chert and at some locations the fossils are hollow and contain small quartz crystals which may be amethystine in colour. The fossils may also be infilled with agate, but specimens are rarely of appreciable size.

Probably the most exotic form of silica to occur in the chert is opal. In the Derbyshire chert, the opal is usually represented by the common yellow variety which does not exhibit opalescence. However, small specimens of truly opalescent opal have been identified amongst the chert beds near the small mining village of Reeth in Swaledale.

Quartz crystals and chalcedony are reasonably common finds amongst lead mining waste on old mine dumps in Durham and Northumberland, and are also common amongst more recent fluorite workings in these areas. Agate patterns in blue, white and yellow may also occur amongst the quartz waste from the mines. It must be stressed, however, that permission to enter any of the present mine workings must be obtained in advance and may not necessarily be forthcoming. Access to older mine dumps is usually more easily obtained.

In terms of the normally accepted gemstones, the Pennines have little to offer. Although opal, agate and amethyst occur, they are only present in insignificant amounts and have little appeal. Despite this, the Pennines have supplied man with a wide range of decorative stones which are truly as individual as the hills from whence they came.

1. Xenoliths are inclusions of pre-existing rock in an igneous rock.

6.   A Collector's Guide

COLLECTING gemstones is a fascinating and rewarding hobby but like any group of people, all collectors have to consider how their hobby affects others. The first thought that any collector should consider is conservation. For this is a time when man is beginning to appreciate the necessity for conservation.

If one person visits a gemstone location and takes away one specimen, then this will probably have little effect on the site in question. However, if a thousand collectors visit a site and everyone takes a specimen, the site may cease to exist. Bearing in mind the nature of gemstone localities and the scarcity of the stones themselves, it is essential that the collector should take only the minimum he requires.

Of course, at beach locations only a limited number of gemstone pebbles are visible at any one time and this fact alone means that a degree of natural conservation is taking place. In any case collecting at a beach location is not likely to damage the location and indeed, specimens left on the beach would continue to be eroded by the sea's action and eventually would be destroyed.

Another, and in some cases the most important consideration, is ownership of the location. Even the most isolated mineral or gemstone location belongs to someone. Mineral waste which was accumulated during the lead mining boom of the 18th and 19th centuries is a prominent feature of the landscape in Northern England, but even the waste mineral has an owner and his or her permission must be sought by any would be searcher. Failure to ask permission before entering a private gemstone location has resulted in the closing of sites in the past. Please remember to ask first, no matter how difficult the owner is to find.

Certain areas of countryside in Northern England belong to the National Trust and collecting is in some cases not permitted. However, collecting which involves picking up loose specimens on a beach is one thing, hacking indiscriminately at a rock face in an attempt to obtain specimens is quite another. Hammering on rock surfaces is definitely to be avoided. In the first place it is probably unnecessary as examples of the appropriate gemstone will usually be available nearby in an eroded form and in the second place, the damage to the scenery can be visually objectionable, and the rock debris dangerous to animals.

Quarries

Permission can often be obtained to enter working quarries and here the collector will frequently find that the hard work has been done for him. By the same token, the explosives which are employed to shatter the rock face in the quarry may also shatter the gemstones or minerals for which the collector searches. It is also worth remembering that walking on recently blasted rock can be dangerous.

In a working quarry where new rock is constantly being exposed, examples of such minerals and gemstones as occur may turn up fairly frequently, but in a disused quarry where new rock faces are not being exposed, specimens may be very hard to find. In addition many old disused quarries have partly returned to nature and become largely overgrown which makes exploration very difficult.

Mines and Mine Tips

It is a regrettable fact that many old and long disused mines are still accessible to anyone, with or without the experience to cope in such potentially dangerous surroundings. One may still stumble upon unguarded mine shafts which may extend hundreds of feet into the ground. Certainly they are a death trap for the unwary.

Old mine workings are no place for collectors without specialist knowledge. It was quite common for miners to stack rock waste in the workings on wooden pallets which have since rotted leaving mounds of unstable rock. It is also possible to find shafts of considerable depth which are only covered by a few rotting planks. In the muddy, murky conditions underground it is easy to walk on to such planks before realizing they are there.

Mine tips may offer a representative selection of the minerals produced by the adjacent mines. Specimens are often weathered due to prolonged exposure to the elements, but good examples may often be found below the surface of the heap where they have been protected by the upper layers.

Beaches

Beach collecting is usually most rewarding in the winter months when rough seas have re-sorted the shingle. In the summer, the shingle is frequently picked over and the tide does the minimum of redistribution. Don't forget to check your tide tables before setting out. The best time to search is on a receding tide.

Rivers and Streams

During the summer months the shingle in a river lies largely undisturbed, and consequently it quickly becomes coated in slime which readily disguises its identity. The best time to search, therefore, is during the winter when rapid movement of the shingle keeps it reasonably clean. It is always a good idea to search the fine shingle first because there you should find gemstone fragments more numerous, and this indicates whether larger finds are likely.

Fields

The need to collect gemstones in farmers' fields will seldom be necessary in Northern England except in the Cheviot Hills where agates occur, and possibly around Retford in Nottinghamshire for the same stone. Fields can only be searched in the winter time after the harvest and before the crops are sown.

After the initial ploughing, everything is coated with a thick film of mud which only the subsequent frost and rain can break down. The best time to search fields, therefore, is during March when the work of the elements is complete.

Collector's Code

This code has been compiled to encourage the best possible relationship with site owners, preserve localities and indicate areas of potential danger.

1. Always obtain permission to enter private locations in advance.
2. Always follow the Country Code.
3. Leave the locality in a safe condition; don't leave plastic bags and tin cans which could injure farm animals.
4. In quarries and gravel pits, avoid walking under the cliff face and on recently blasted rock which may be unstable.
5. When exploring mine dumps, beware of inadequately guarded shafts.
6. Consult the tide tables before exploring beaches.
7. Do not hammer on exposed rock faces.
8. Never collect more specimens than you need. Leave some for the next person.

Equipment

A useful selection of equipment can fairly easily be amassed and should be made up as follows:—

Geologist's hammer, cold chisel, safety glasses, haversack and wrapping materials (newspaper for delicate specimens). Geological maps of the drift variety show all the rocks at the surface, including the glacial deposits and are very useful. An Ordnance Survey map of the same scale is useful in pinpointing the rocks on the geological map.

7. Lapidary, the Art of Polishing Stones

MANY gemstones are beautiful in their own right, but others require polishing to achieve the beauty of which they are capable. How many of us have picked up an attractive pebble off a beach, little realising that its beauty was largely due to the fact that it was wet? When dry the pebble would not have attracted attention. Polishing a stone simply preserves the wet look which a stone has on the beach.

The polishing of a stone is carried out in three basic operations. The first stage involves grinding out all the imperfections and irregularities in a stone, using a coarse abrasive. Once all the imperfections have been removed, the stone is ground with successively finer grades of abrasives, each removing the scratches left by the preceding coarser grade. The final stage is to polish the stone using a tin oxide or cerium oxide, which brings up the final polish. Silicon carbide is the most common abrasive and the grades from coarse to fine are 80, 220, 400, 600.

The process may be carried out either by hand, which is time consuming, and can be costly, using grinding and polishing equipment, or using a tumble polishing machine. The tumbler, as it is called, takes approximately five weeks to complete the process when polishing pebbles, but much longer for rough stone. These are reasonably inexpensive machines, and of course no skill is required. The stones spend approximately one week in each stage and providing every stone and the barrel are well washed out between stages, no problems should result.

A tumbler can only be utilized for polishing hard stones like quartz, such soft stones as jet or Blue John would rapidly be worn away by the tumbling action. Soft stones were traditionally worked by hand, using natural sandstones as abrasives. Today silicon carbide has taken over from the sandstones, and bonded grinding wheels are used on electrically powered machines. It is interesting to reflect on some of the treadle machines of the last century on which the most sophisticated work was completed.

Cutting stone today is done with a diamond saw. This consists of a mild steel disc shaped like a circular saw but without teeth. Instead the diamond blade has a thick rim which contains industrial diamond. The blade is, in fact, a thin grinding wheel and grinds its way through the stones. Naturally the blade is attached to a machine which includes an oil coolant. Diamond blades range from 4 inches to over 3 foot in diameter, but diamonds in any form are expensive and the larger blades only have industrial use.

Cutting stones in the last century was chiefly accomplished using a wire saw. The wire was continually worked against the stone while being fed with abrasive particles which did the actual cutting. This technique was quite satisfactory, especially with the relatively soft limestones. Much patience would be required while waiting for such a machine to cut a hard gemstone.

Many vases and other ornaments still exist which were manufactured during the 18th and 19th centuries in Blue John and limestone. These were turned on a lathe into the basic shape and subsequently hollowed out and polished. Large vases were usually made in sections and then assembled; there is however one large bowl which was manufactured from one piece of Blue John. This bowl is on display at Chatsworth House in Derbyshire.

The only lathe tool available to the earlier craftsman was a tempered steel bar made from fine quality steel. The bar usually measured between 24 inches and 30 inches in length and was ¾ inch square. Today better quality steel is available and the development of tungsten carbide and diamond lathe tools have greatly increased the efficiency and speed with which items in stone can be worked on a lathe.

This type of lapidary work is preferably accomplished on an old lathe which has ceased to be sufficiently precise for engineering purposes. Small lathes which have concluded their normal working life can often be purchased at very reasonable prices by anyone wishing to try their hand at turning stone. However, turning the softer stones can also be accomplished on a woodworking lathe. Turning such hard gemstones as agate is not easily accomplished in the home and it is strongly recommended that enthusiasts work with the softer stones such as limestone and alabaster.

Turning stone on a lathe can result in a wide range of products ranging from table lamps to clocks, barometers and candle holders. The shape can be as intricate or as simple as the craftsman wishes. No artisitic ability is required although turning stone can be a lengthy process which requires a considerable amount of patience.

Inlay work is not carried out by many today, primarily because it is labour intensive. The basic technique was to take a flat panel of limestone approximately a ¼ inch thick. Having marked out a pattern on the panel, the next operation was to fret-cut areas of the limestone to give a number of precisely shaped spaces. Pieces of gemstone were then cut and ground to the same size and shape as the spaces in the panel. The shaped pieces were then set into the spaces in the panel to complete the inlay which was then ground smooth and polished.

The popularity of Whitby jet was, to a large extent, created by the mourning tradition, but even today there is a place in jewellery for a black stone. However, as a soft stone jet was capable of being carved into delicate yet intricate designs. Looking back, the jet carvings, which were possibly at their most popular as brooches, were typical of the Victorian Era in which they were produced.

The fact that quite large amounts of Victorian jet jewellery are still available today reflects the current fashions into which jet does not easily fit. However this does not detract from the tremendous artistry which went into the creation of so many beautiful carvings. The fine steel tools available to the old craftsmen have now been replaced by diamond tools but here, and for the first time in this revue of lapidary techniques, we find the signs of real skill. Unlike most of the other lapidary processes I have described, carving is a skill which relies to a large extent upon natural talent and ability.

Today lapidary is a popular hobby in Britain. Thousands of people have purchased tumble polishing machines and there is a hard core of enthusiasts who have obtained exotic equipment for cutting, shaping and polishing stones. The old skills which were once the basis of quite large stone working industries in Northern England, after lying dormant for almost a hundred years, are now being practised once again on an amateur scale. The satisfaction of taking a rough, angular piece of stone and transforming it into an item of beauty is immense. You could do worse than to give it a try!

BIBLIOGRAPHY AND FURTHER READING

Bauer, J., *Minerals, Rocks and Precious Stones,* Octopus, London, 1974.

Bennison and Wright, *The Geological History of the British Isles,* Edward Arnold, London, 1969.

Cooper, D., and Battershill, N., *Victorian Sentimental Jewellery,* David and Charles, Newton Abbot, 1972.

Deeson, A. F. L., (editor) *The Collectors' Encyclopedia of Rocks and Minerals,* David and Charles, Newton Abbot, 1973.

Downie, C., and Neves, R., (editors) *Geological Excursions in the Sheffield Region,* Sheffield University, 1967.

Edwards, W., and Trotter, F. M., *British Regional Geology: The Pennines and Adjacent Areas,* H.M.S.O., London, 1954.

Ellis, C., *The Pebbles on the Beach,* Faber and Faber, London, 1957.

Greg, R. P., and Lettsom, W. G., *Manual of the Mineralogy of Great Britain and Ireland,* John Van Voorst, London, 1858.

Holland, H. D., *Granites, Solutions and Base Metal Deposits,* Econ. Geol. 67, pp. 281-301, 1972.

Holmes, A., *Principles of Physical Geology,* Thomas Nelson and Sons, London, 1944.

Kirkham, N., *Derbyshire Lead Mining Through the Centuries,* Bradford Barton, Truro, 1968.

Mitchell, G. H., *The Geological History of the Lake District,* Proc. Yorks. Geol. Soc. 30, pp. 407-463, 1956.

Mueller, G., *A Genetical and Geochemical Survey of the Derbyshire Mineral Deposits,* Unpublished Ph.D. thesis in the University of London, 1951.

Park and MacDiarmid, *Ore Deposits,* W. H. Freeman, 1975.

Raistrick, A., *Ice Age in Yorkshire,* Dalesman, 1968.

Raistrick, A., and Jennings, B., *A history of lead mining in the Pennines,* XXX, pp. 347, Longmans, London, 1965.

Rodgers, P. R., *Agate Collecting in Britain,* B. T. Batsford, 1975.

Rodgers, P. R., *Yorkshire Minerals,* Dalesman, 1975.

Rodgers, P. R., *Derbyshire Geology,* Dalesman, 1977.

Rodgers, P. R., *Geology of the Yorkshire Dales,* Dalesman, 1979.

Rodgers, P. R., *Rock and Mineral Collecting in Britain,* Faber & Faber, 1979.

Rodgers, P. R., and Muir Wood, R., *On the Rocks, A Geology of Britain,* B.B.C. Publications, 1978.

Shackleton, E. H., *Lakeland Geology,* Dalesman, 1966.

Sinkanas, J., *Gem Cutting, A Lapidary Manual,* D. Van Nostrand, Princetown, New Jersey, 1962.

Taylor, Burgess, Land, Mills, Smith and Warren, *British Regional Geology, Northern England,* H.M.S.O., London, 1971.

Wilcockson, W. H., *Igneous Rocks and Mineralization of the High Peak of Derbyshire,* Proc. Geol. Assoc. 43, pp. 184-191, 1932.

Index